Towards an Efficient Allocation of Electrical Energy

Towards an Efficient Allocation of Electrical Energy

An Essay in Applied Welfare Economics

Noel D. Uri
U.S. Department of Labor
Bureau of Labor Statistics

Lexington Books
D.C. Heath and Company
Lexington, Massachusetts
Toronto London

Library of Congress Cataloging in Publication Data

Uri, Noel D
Towards an efficient allocation of electrical energy.

Bibliography: p.
Includes index.
1. Electric utilities—United States. 2. Electric utilities—United States—Costs. I. Title.
HD9685.U5U75 333.7 74-22194
ISBN 0-669-96826-9

Published simultaneously in Canada

Printed in the United States of America

International Standard Book Number: 0-669-96826-9

Library of Congress Catalog Card Number: 74-22194

To Pop

Contents

List of Figure and Tables

Figure

Tables

Preface

Growing demand, increasing costs, and changing social values are combining to place increasing stress on the electrical energy industry in the United States. Recurrent and spreading power shortages are in the foreseeable future unless positive steps are taken to remedy conditions inhibiting the efficient development of generating capacity. Similarly, increasing prices for electrical energy seem to be the future norm rather than the declining prices that have been the general experience of the past. Operation and maintenance costs and fuel costs are being forced up by market pressure at a faster rate than they are being offset by technological developments that reduce costs. Since the industry has a large base of imbedded capital investment, which acts to dilute the increased cost of investment in new generating plant and equipment, and because of time lags in rate adjustment procedures, the cost increases of the past few years are just now being translated into rate increases.

It is already too late to circumvent further difficulties. Investment in new equipment cannot take place instantaneously, so it will take time to correct inadequacies in generating capacity. Demand for electrical energy continues to grow unabated. In such a situation something must give, and what has been yielding has been the margin of assurance of service. Voltage reductions and a few localized blackouts occurred in several of the nation's major urban areas during recent years when utilities were obliged to reduce or shed loads during peak demand periods to avoid overloading the system.

Within the context of these difficulties, opportunities exist for increasing the efficiency with which electrical energy is generated and allocated. Congruent with this is the realization that, for electrical energy, development planning is a continuous and sequential process involving mobilization and efficient use of resources. The important aspect of development planning in the electrical energy sector is the formulation of suitable policies to carry out the economic activities of generating, transmitting and distributing, and consuming over time and over space.

The tools of the economist are sufficiently well developed to investigate the problems mentioned above. It is hoped that in a normative way, the recommendations will be considered by policy makers, and in a positive way, the methodology will be closely scrutinized by the individuals responsible for investment decisions in the electrical energy industry. However, this last group should temper their analysis with the realization that throughout this work, attention is concentrated on the basic economic aspects of the problem. It must be clearly understood that the discussion pays little attention to many aspects of practical engineering that necessarily loom large in the eyes of those who face the technical side of the problem.

Throughout the course of any work, one becomes indebted to many different people. This study is no exception, and I would like to take this opportunity to thank openly two people to whom I owe the greatest gratitude. First, T. Takayama of the University of Illinois has shown a great interest in the problem and its formulation and has been unstinting in his willingness to listen and offer invaluable suggestions as to the application of intertemporal-spacial price equilibrium models. Second, Allen Wyse of Duke University has been of immense assistance by raising points that helped me to clarify the formulation and to recognize some of the inherent limitations of this study.

Finally, the views expressed here are my own and do not necessarily reflect the policies of the organizations with which I have been and currently am associated.

1 Introduction

Abundant electrical energy at low cost is essential to a highly industrialized economy like that of the United States. It is difficult to visualize the American way of life without air conditioners, aluminum cans, and neon lights: it is equally difficult to imagine substitutes for these characteristics of American society if cheap electrical energy were no longer available.

With the existing and growing dependence on electrical energy, there has been a great deal of anxiety over the sufficiency of the nation's resources for meeting the apparently insatiable demand for electrical energy.[1] Recently, the concern over energy[2] has been embedded in a more general pessimism about the viability of economic growth on a finite world.[3] This new and pejorative view of economic growth holds that growth is bounded by a finite amount of essential, exhaustible natural resources. In the process of consuming finite resources, the standard of living descends toward subsistence.

If such a sequence is plausible, the squeeze will most likely be felt in the energy sector first. Energy, and specifically electrical energy, is a necessary input in many processes. Although more judicious usage might save some energy, it is not possible to produce aluminum or run electrical machinery without it. With the exception of food, no other single commodity is so fundamental as energy, of which electrical energy is a significant component.[4]

Opportunities exist for significantly increasing the efficiency with which electrical energy is generated and allocated in the United States. This is the concern of this book. The focus is on efficiency to the exclusion of distributional equity considerations.[5] Further, attention throughout is concentrated on the basic economic aspects of the problem, and it must be clearly understood that the discussion pays little attention to the practical engineering problems that necessarily loom large in the eyes of those whose job it is to face the technical aspects of the situation.

In the United States the price of electrical energy has for the most part been determined by market forces. The qualification in this statement is due to the biases of utility companies with local roots, perspectives, and organizational foundations. Ostensibly, political structures exist to facilitate the definition of the proper scope of institutional coordination at the national level. At the present time, however, national coordination of the electrical energy industry seems more a myth than a reality. The unhappy history of the Federal Power Commission in the United States, even though it was originally designed to be a functional coordinator, shows that it has tended to be a lobbyist for the producer versus the consumer, and the role of mediator is betrayed for that of clandestine advocate.[6]

Recently there has been much discussion arguing for a more concerted effort at coordination of the generation and distribution of electrical energy in an effort to let market forces truly determine the price. In the proposed Electric Power Coordination Act of 1971, for example, it was decreed that "the public interest requires that utility managements recognize their joint, cooperative responsibility to assure an abundant supply of electric energy to satisfy public demands with the greatest possible economy."[7] The good intent and the technical apparatus are available to accomplish this coordination. However, the possibility of seeing this coordination come to fruition in a reasonable period of time is remote. A piece of legislation introduced in the 93rd Congress, H.R. 1258, is designed to oversee this coordination, but no action has been taken, and it is doubtful any will be taken on the bill.[8]

This will not deter present considerations. By looking at a unified market, consisting of the entire United States and its distinguishing regions, one can look at electrical energy pricing and allocation on a national scale. The intellectual basis for allowing market determination of prices lies in the theory of general economic equilibrium. This theory assumes that there are consumers with initial resources and given preferences and producers operating with well-defined technical relations. The theory can encompass many time periods, but it assumes convex production and preference sets, and that markets exist for all goods, services, and contingencies.[9] This means there must be futures markets, say, for electrical energy in 1990. Also, all the costs and benefits of producing electrical energy must be internalized to the decision maker. Under these conditions, a market system will have a general equilibrium of prices and quantities. The equilibrium will be efficient in the sense that there is no way of improving the lot of one consumer without worsening the lot of another. (i.e., the system is Pareto-optimal.) Stated alternately, prices are appropriate indicators of social scarcity given the preferences and initial endowments of society.

Background

The electrical energy industry is characterized by a separation of supply and demand locations and by a fixed amount of transmission capacity available at any one time. In light of the preceding efficiency considerations, a model will be developed and discussed that is capable of dealing with these characteristics.

Over twenty years ago, Stephen Enke considered in a purely descriptive framework how one good would be traded among several spatially separated markets. He argued that by assuming regions are separated but not isolated by a volume-dependent transportation cost per physical unit, assuming that there are no legal restrictions to limit the actions of the profit seeking traders of each region, assuming that for each region the functions relating to local production and local use are given, and assuming that transportation cost is known, one can ascertain: (1) the net price in each region, (2) the quantity of exports or imports for each region, (3) which regions export, import, or do neither, (4) the volume and direction of trade between all possible regions.[10]

Samuelson considered this spatial problem, casting Enke's descriptive formulation mathematically into a maximum problem and related this specification to a standard problem in linear programming, the so-called Koopmans-Hitchcock minimum-transport-cost problem.[11] Samuelson then suggested that after the problem in descriptive price behavior has been converted into a maximum problem, it can be solved by trial and error or by a systematic procedure of varying shipments in the direction of increasing social payoff, which is defined for a given region as the algebraic area under its excess-demand curve.

Takayama and Judge restated the Samuelson partial-equilibrium (one commodity) formulation disregarding the interdependencies with other commodities and concentrating on the interdependencies that exist between the different markets in the production, pricing, and use of the one commodity.[12] This is accomplished by postulating appropriate linear dependencies between regional supply, demand, and price and converting the Enke-Samuelson specification into a quadratic programming problem. The existence of aggregate linear regional demand and supply relations are assumed. The formulation was restated by Takayama and Woodland, clarifying the relationship between various price and quantity formulations. The problem was stated in its primal and "purified" dual form, i.e., entirely in terms of either price variables or in terms of quantity variables.[13]

Noting that economic relations in time have many of the properties of economic relations in space, Samuelson in subsequent work discussed the problem of intertemporal price equilibrium and suggested how the tools for analyzing spatial competitive relations might be applied to the more complex problems of equilibrium commodity prices over time.[14] This problem is much more complex because the theory is inextricably bound up with uncertainty. It is assumed for simplicity's sake that future conditions are foreseeable and foreseen.

Operating with these considerations, Takayama and Judge extend their spatial formulation to obtain the competitive price and product allocation when markets are separated by both space and time.[15] In particular, the concept of net social payoff (social payoff less total transport cost) is used as a basis for deducing the conditions of spatial and intertemporal equilibrium and, given linear dependencies between regional supply, demand, and price for each time period and given transportation cost among regions and storage cost from time period t to time period $t + 1$, the problem is converted into a quadratic programming problem that can be solved directly for a competitive solution.

A methodological note on the use of the economic surplus should be inserted at this point. The entire intertemporal-spatial problem formulation rests on the concept of net social payoff—consumers' plus producers' surplus less total transport cost and total storage cost. A rejection of the viability of the economic surplus concept of necessity, it may be argued, leads to a rejection of the entire intertemporal-spatial framework as developed by Takayama and Judge. The arguments for and against the economic surplus concept are long and heated.[16] It is not the purpose here to attempt any justification for the use of the concept. It is simply observed that while it is easy to raise objections to the use of the concept of economic surplus, it is difficult to find any workable alternative.

As a final comment on the methodology adopted here, observe, as Bhagwati has stressed, that the measurement of losses and gains from changes in policy has resulted from pressure on economists to provide such measures. Policies are maintained or changed largely for noneconomic reasons; though the magnitude of the (economic) cost involved is commonly demanded and considered in discussions of public policy. Whether one likes it or not, this is what the decision maker wants. In consonance with the best traditions in the profession, the theorist has begun to meet this need in an attempt to bring economic analysis closer to fulfilling the objective that provides its ultimate reason for existence. The result has been a definite and significant trend towards measurement of welfare change.[17]

Qualifications and Limitations

In an attempt to determine an efficient allocation and pricing of electrical energy, a intertemporal-spatial model of the Takayama-Judge type is developed. The electrical energy industry as a whole has distinguishing characteristics that necessitate a departure from the strict linear demand-linear supply relationships. The model is not cast in a general equilibrium framework. Other markets are considered to be outside of the investigation. This implies that certain unknowns are taken as given and due to this "ceteris paribus" assumption, a simplified or partial equilibrium situation is faced that is defined as an intertemporal-spatial price equilibrium.[18] If it turns out that these other markets do not fulfill the optimality conditions,[19] then globally the allocation and pricing of electrical energy resulting from the intertemporal-spatial model might not be efficient. Consequently, be cautioned that when the concept of efficiency is discussed, it is in this partial equilibrium setting.

When determining allocation and resultant pricing considerations, one must not be bound by the legal and administrative critera that previously controlled decisions. This is not to imply that such constraints cannot be imposed on the model. The model is flexible enough to allow the incorporation of such considerations. However, as long as economic efficiency is the focal point, legal and administrative criteria will be excluded.

The allocation that will lead to increased efficiency rests on the normative formulation of the problem. The intertemporal-spatial equilibrium model used normatively shows how the output of electrical energy at many locations should flow to many consuming areas if competitive conditions are to be attained and costs minimized. If one is to produce quantitative statements describing the existing competitive markets and predict the future course of economic variables (positive economics), a positive model of intertemporal-spatial equilibrium is required.[20] From the positive economics point of view, an intertemporal-spatial model is a competitive economic model in which the economic system may be described by a set of simultaneous equations including aggregate demand for each good by consumers for each market, the aggregate supply of each good by producers for each market, the distribution activities over space, and equilibrium conditions. If a simultaneous solution of exogenously estimated structural equations were intended as a positive analysis, it would be subject to Haavelmo's criticism.[21] Unfortunately, a model of the electrical energy sector does not lend itself to this simultaneous system approach and hence the intertemporal-spatial price equilibrium model must be interpreted in a normative sense.

Optimality Conditions

Given that electrical energy is regulated by a plethora of state agencies and the Federal Power Commission, the intertemporal-spatial price equilibrium model assumes that a unified authority responsible for the allocation and pricing of electrical energy does not act as a monopolist in seeking to maximize profits but rather sets a policy that will maximize social welfare in relation to available and future electrical energy supplies. As a matter of fact, the electrical energy industry was brought within the regulatory sphere so that the public could capture the efficiency benefits of this natural monopoly while avoiding the less desirable tendencies of monopolists to limit output and charge higher than the competitive norm.[22] Kahn argues that the single most widely accepted rule for governing the regulated industries is to regulate them in such a way as to produce the same result as would be produced by effective competition, if it were feasible.[23] Generally, the economist would advise that the maximum social welfare in a regulated market would be obtained by requiring each single producing unit to produce up to the point at which the cost of the last unit produced equals the price that consumers are willing to pay for this level of production.

One of the characteristics, however, of the electrical energy industry as a natural monopoly is that the long-run marginal cost of the firm is falling throughout the relevant range of output. In this instance the economist's prescription of setting price equal to long-run marginal cost may not cover the total cost of production, and a subsidy of some form might be required. Regulators are either unable or unwilling to use this means to achieve the efficient allocation of resources. Consequently, a price structure is developed which ostensibly takes advantage of differing elasticities of demand among various categories of consumers. Price discrimination permits the utility to recover its full costs plus its allowed rate of return.[24]

Putting aside the actual relation of costs to prices, costs remain the most significant consideration in the economic analysis. Further, the electrical energy industry is a decreasing cost industry. That is, the industry confronts a long-run average cost curve whereby at any given point in time and for a given level of technology, the unit cost of a large output is less than that for a smaller one.[25] Such a cost curve exhibits increasing returns to scale. Additionally, technological change may occur, in which case it is again possible to find decreasing costs over time as the average cost curve drifts downward.[26]

For reasons not having to do with the economic principles involved, regulatory commissions have generally rejected the use of a subsidy to make up for losses that would result from the implementation of long-run marginal cost pricing. Instead, regulators and the electrical energy industry have made use of a value of service pricing concept. Under this principle differential rates based upon willingness to pay were established by public utilities and generally approved as recommended by regulatory commissions. As a result, a practice has evolved akin to the pricing scheme a discriminating monopolist might employ for different classes of customers.[27]

Summarily, one sees what optimum price-allocation rule should be followed and what, de facto, is followed. It remains to be seen what society as a whole pays for this inefficiency.

The Spatial and Temporal Setting

The ideal spatial setting for the model of electrical energy that is to be developed would be the location of the individual consuming and producing unit. This is not feasible. Data limitations prohibit this setting as well as several other potential settings. The spatial setting that is viable is the Bureau of the Census' nine region division of the contiguous United States. This categorization can be found in Table 1-1. The regional grouping of states is based on a comparison of income payments; industrial distribution of employment; population size, distribution, and growth; racial and ethnic composition; level of living; transportation and communication; health; and history.[28]

Within each region three consumer sectors (residential, commercial, and industrial) will be considered. Each of these three sectors exhibit a distinguishable demand for electrical energy. There is a fourth sector, nominally called "other," consisting of transportation use, government use, agricultural use, railroad use, and interdepartmental use (energy used by the utilities themselves), that, across regions, accounted in 1970 for about 4.2 percent of total electrical energy consumed. Because of its minuscule proportion, heterogeneous composition, and overall unresponsiveness to price changes (i.e., its demand is almost perfectly inelastic), the "other" sector will be pushed into the background of consideration, where it will be assumed that the sector can purchase all it desires at the prevailing market price. This assumption will tend to understate slightly the estimated value of the net social payoff.

On the supply side, three alternate methods of generating electrical energy will be considered. Closely involved with rapid increases in demand is the problem of determining optimal investment policies in new plants and equipment. Investment decision variables of the industry interact strongly at a point in time and over time because different energy sources have complementary functions in the interconnected power system and because the optimal balance will depend on the existing and expected structure of the system. The structure of the system rests on the mix of hydroelectric schemes, fossil-fueled steam-electric plants (coal, oil, and gas), and nuclear-steam reactors. These are the main sources of electrical energy generation. A fourth method of generating electrical energy, internal combustion, is not incorporated into the model. In 1970 it accounted for only 0.396 percent of the electrical energy generated in the United States and is extremely inefficient (on a heat basis). The principal applications of internal combustion generators include meeting peak loads, standby service, emergency power, and reserve.[29]

It is now evident that the concurrence of various increasing needs for energy emphasizes the requirement for coordinated national policy de-

Table 1-1
Regional Classification

Region	*Composition*
1. New England	Maine, New Hampshire, Vermont, Massachusetts, Rhode Island, Connecticut
2. Middle Atlantic	New York, New Jersey, Pennsylvania
3. East North Central	Ohio, Indiana, Illinois, Michigan, Wisconsin
4. West North Central	Minnesota, Iowa, Missouri, North Dakota, South Dakota, Nebraska, Kansas
5. South Atlantic	Delaware, Maryland, District of Columbia, Virginia, West Virginia, North Carolina, South Carolina, Georgia, Florida
6. East South Central	Kentucky, Tennessee, Alabama, Mississippi
7. West South Central	Arkansas, Louisana, Oklahoma, Texas
8. Mountain	Montana, Idaho, Wyoming, Colorado, New Mexico, Arizona, Utah, Nevada
9. Pacific	Washington, Oregon, California

velopment. The national demand for electrical energy has followed the pattern of doubling approximately every ten years. A further doubling of demand during the 1970s appears virtually certain and a growth rate only slightly less steep is presently indicated for the 1980s. This rate of growth far outdistances that of energy consumption in general. In 1960, 20 percent of the energy consumed in the United States was in the form of electrical energy. By 1980 electrical energy's share of national energy use is expected to pass the 30 percent mark, and by 1990 it is expected to be approximately 41 percent.[30] Consequently, there is a real need to look at the longer range problems. To this end, the period 1970 to 1990 will be focused on at five year intervals.

Overview

The objective of this study then is to show quantitatively that opportunities exist for markedly increasing the efficiency of pricing and allocating electrical energy in the United States. The approach will be through an intertemporal-spatial price equilibrium model. Chapter 2 and Chapter 3 will look at demand considerations while Chapters 4 and 5 look at interregional transmission, distribution, and supply considerations. Chapter 6 presents the model, complete with its empirical solution. Chapter 7 summarizes and concludes the study.

2 Estimation of Demand

One of the basic assumptions underlying the economic environment of the intertemporal-spatial price equilibrium model is that the demand functions for electrical energy for each region during each time period are known with certainty or are available in the certainty equivalence sense.[1] The intertemporal-spatial price equilibrium model used in this investigation, in its generalized form, hypothesizes linear price-dependent demand relations. This chapter details the theoretical rationale underlying the estimation procedure, while the following chapter presents the estimates of linear demand for electrical energy in the United States that will be used in the model.

Background

It is necessary to know the demand curves in a simple price and quantity form. One cannot estimate, however, such a simple relationship and expect to get meaningful results. The identification problem presents an insurmountable obstacle.[2] Consequently, an indirect approach is used. After some preliminary analyses, it was determined that a variable elasticity model represents most accurately economic reality. The elasticities obtained are then used to secure point estimates of the requisite demand functions.

Before the specific estimating procedure is examined a brief look at the theoretical justification of single equation analysis is needed. It should be noted that the variable elasticity model does not satisfy the classical theory of demand exactly.[3] However, despite its defects, especially that of nonadditivity,[4] this functional form is without rival with regard to goodness of fit, ease of estimation, and immediacy of interpretation.[5] Further, reliable data are available in the required form allowing one to perform the desired calculations forthwith. The particular market conditions of electrical energy favor single equation analyses. The reason is that prices are largely set by public regulation and governed by policies as to what is in the public interest rather than by cost or supply considerations alone. As a result, price may be regarded as a predetermined variable, at any rate in the short run.[6] Specifically, since the variables that are found on the right hand side are predetermined, the "reduced form" parameters can be estimated directly. Clearly no identification problem exists. In this model of the demand for electrical energy, the market operates via quantity adjustment as opposed to the case where the quantity is set and price varies.

Demand Model

It is initially assumed that the demand for electrical energy is determined by four factors in addition to the price of electrical energy: population, per capita personal income, the price of substitute fuels (gas), and the price of complementary products such as household appliances (for the residential sector) or of machinery (for the commercial and industrial sectors).

The purpose of the analysis necessarily affects the form. In particular, the reason for obtaining an estimate of the demand elasticities will affect the level of the analysis: state, regional, or national. Given that the primary concern is the general question of interregional flows, it seems that the economically relevant entity is the region.[7]

Annual values of the explanatory factors, especially per capita income, population, and the price of electrical energy exhibit strong trend components between 1947 and 1970. Hence, the correlation between all factors is high, which makes estimation of the elasticities difficult. Further, even though a model provides a good fit to the available data, this does not necessarily imply that projections of future demand using the model are reliable. This is particularly true in the consideration of electrical energy since the levels of the explanatory factors are not precisely following established trends.

Preliminary results suggest that good estimates of the elasticities cannot be obtained from a single time series of observations of a sector in a region.[8] Alternately, estimates derived from a single cross section of observations are not satisfactory for making projections over time. Hence, both cross-section (regions) and time-series (years) observations are pooled to provide a suitable basis for estimation. With this pooling, the relative error variance of the resulting elasticity estimates will decrease; i.e., the estimates are more efficient.[9]

The use of cross-section data presents another problem. Ordinary estimation procedures are statistically justified for a constant elasticity model only if the elasticity of each variable is equal in each region. Under the more realistic specification that differences do exist between regions, the use of constant elasticity estimates can be questioned.[10] For this reason, a variable elasticity model is used in an effort to capture some of this heterogeneity between regions. Additionally, models for three consumer sectors (residential, commercial, and industrial) are estimated separately.

Another specification problem comes about because the equilibrium level of the dependent variable will not be attained until some time after the change in the independent variable has occurred. Consequently, it is necessary to superimpose on the original model specification, a second hypothesis concerning the time patterns of adjustment of dependent to independent variables.[11] The lag reflects the relationship between the use of electrical energy and existing stocks of electrical appliances and machinery. The level of these stocks depends on past and current decisions and therefore on the size of past and current independent variables. If the lag in demand is ignored, the estimates of the elasticities are biased[12] and inconsistent.[13]

A geometric lag structure is specified in the model employed and two estimation procedures are used. The model may be written for a particular sector, region, and year as follows:

$$y_{ijt} = A_{ij} y_{ij(t-1)}^{\phi_i} V_{1ijt}^{\pi_{1i}} \ . \ . \ . \ V_{nijt}^{\pi_{ni}} e^{\delta_{1i}/V_{1ijt}} \ . \ . \ . \ e^{\delta_{ni}/V_{nijt}} e^{\epsilon_{ijt}} \tag{2.1}$$

where e = the base of natural logarithm,

i = ith sector,

j = jth region,

t = tth year,

y = the quantity of electrical energy demanded,

V_k = the level of the kth causal factor,

$A, \phi, \pi_1, \ldots, \pi_n, \delta_1, \ldots, \delta_n$ are unknown parameters and

ϵ is the error term.

This specification is a simple generalization of the constant elasticity model implying that each elasticity varies as the level of the corresponding factor varies. The elasticity for the kth factor in the ith sector is $[\pi_{ki} - (\delta_{ki}/V_{ki})]$. A level of V_{ki} must be specified when the elasticity is evaluated, since the value changes as δ_{ki}/V_{ki} changes. As the value of V_{ki} increases, the elasticity approaches π_{ki} asymptotically. If V_{ki} decreases towards zero, the elasticity approaches a negative infinity. The levels of all predetermined variables are expected to expand in the future and hence the relative stable behavior of the elasticities is desirable.

The implication of the model is simply that different values of a particular elasticity between regions can be explained by the level of the corresponding factor in each region. A further insight into the model is obtained by looking at ϕ_i. It is expected that the value of this parameter is between 0 and 1. Observe that $1 - \phi_i$ is the proportion of the demand response completed in the first year. If ϕ_i is close to 0, demand adjusts quickly to changes in the causal factors, while a ϕ_i close to 1 implies a slower adjustment of demand.[14] This can be seen more clearly in the following sections.

Estimation Techniques

The objective of this chapter is to estimate the parameters of the demand equations and deduce the elasticities. To accomplish this task, the functional specification can be linearized using a simple logarithmic (log to the base e) transformation so that

$$\log y_{ijt} = a_{ij} + \phi_i \log y_{ij(t-1)} + \sum_{k=1}^{n} \pi_{ki} \log V_{kijt} + \sum_{k=1}^{n} \delta_{ki}/V_{kijt} + \epsilon_{ijt} \quad (2.2)$$

where a_{ij} = $\log A_{ij}$, and

ϵ_{ijt} = the error term.

Several regression techniques can be used to estimate the parameters of equation (2.2). The behavior of the error terms determine the procedure with the best statistical properties. Before it was decided to pool the cross-section and time-series data, the seemingly unrelated regression technique of Zellner[15] was employed, but most reasonable functional specifications fit the data so well that when the inversion of the variance-covariance matrix was attempted, a near singular matrix was encountered and the computer program could not perform the required operation. Thus, the approach was discarded.

Balestra and Nerlove have proposed a technique for estimating models when cross-section and time-series data are pooled. The basic assumption is that the error term is composed of one component associated with the cross-sectional units, one component associated with the time-series units, and a third varying in both dimensions.[16] Reluctance to use this method is based on two considerations. First, increased efficiency of the estimates is noticeable only if the residual variation is relatively large, which certainly is not the case here. Second, in the case of electrical energy, it does not make economic sense to assume that the a_{ij}'s are constant across regions.[17] Each part of the country produces and consumes a qualitatively unique share of the United States total output, and this is reflected in its demand for electrical energy. For example, the aluminum industry has a tremendous demand for electrical energy and shifted in the late 1940s to the Pacific Northwest where the needed supply was available. In the West South Central region, the price relationship that exists between gas and electrical energy is highly favorable to gas.[18] Other examples can be cited. The point is just that the variance component model is rejected in favor of the separate constant model because the latter seems better to capture this structural phenomena.

Houthakker, Verlager and Scheehan use the error components technique of Balestra and Nerlove because it provides a more consistent estimate of the coefficient on the lagged dependent variable.[19] The advantage achieved is at the expense of a poorer fit as well as its being subject to the aforementioned reservations. Note that their results are not directly comparable to the ones used in this study because a different level of resolution of the data is used.

The estimation of the separate constant term model is done via use of dummy variables that identify each of the nine regions in the United States. To obtain determinate estimates, the additional constraint of omitting the ninth dummy variable was included.[20] The estimated values on the dummy variables are then collapsed into the constant term explaining the difference in each a_{ij}.

Estimates in most regression analyses are obtained using ordinary least squares (OLS). The existence of a lagged dependent variable in the specification makes the reliability of OLS sensitive to the residual specification. The consistency of OLS holds only if the residuals are not serially correlated. If the residuals exhibit any interdependence through time, the OLS estimate is inconsistent.[21]. Consequently, another procedure, instrumental variables, is used in addition to OLS. The instrumental variable estimates are computed,[22] but the values obtained are not economically realistic and therefore they are discarded. This is discussed more fully in the following section.

Empirical Results

The demand model is estimated for the three dominant classes of consumers that can be identified: (1) residential, (2) commercial, and (3) industrial. Annual observations of each variable in the model were obtained for nine regions in the United States from 1947 to 1970. The exact specifications of the variables found to be significant in explaining the demand for electrical energy are presented in Table 2-1. The demand model is a single equation model for each consumer sector. It has been argued in

Table 2-1
Specification of Variables and Their Sources Used in Estimation

Variable	*Consumer Sector*	*Units of Measurement*
Quantity Demanded[a]	1,2,3	Millions of kilowatt hours (kWh)
Per Capita Personal Income[b]	Same	Thousands of 1970 dollars per capita
Price of Electrical Energy[c]	1,2,3	Average mills/kWh in 1970 dollars
Price of Gas[d,e]	1,2,3	Average 1970 dollars per thousand therms (lagged one year)

[a]Source: Edison Electric Institute, *Statistical Yearbook of the Electric Utility Industry,* New York, various years.

[b]Source: For income, Graham, R.E., et.al., "State Projection of Income, Employment, and Population," *Survey of Current Business,* vol. 52, no. 4, and for population, U.S. Department of Commerce, Bureau of Economic Analysis *Statistical Abstract of the United States* U.S. Government Printing Office, Washington, 1971. Note that per capita personal income equals income divided by population.

[c]Source: Edison Electric Institute, *Statistical Yearbook,* various years.

[d]Source: American Gas Association, *Gas Facts Yearbook,* New York, various years.

[e]Includes natural, liquid petroleum, manufactured and mixed gas. Natural gas though is the largest component.

an earlier section that for electrical energy this is an appropriate specification. The one question that arises however is whether average or marginal prices should be used, since a typical rate schedule implies that large-scale users pay lower prices (decreasing block rates).[23]

The choice between average and marginal prices has been considered by Wilson.[24] In economic theory the decision of the individual is based on marginal values, and hence Wilson favors this approach. Alternately, average prices are more practical in importance to utility companies. Maintaining stability between average prices and average costs is the practice of the regulatory agencies, who obtain this by changing the existing rate schedule. In the model used here, average prices are preferred. The results presented by Wilson suggest that using estimates derived based on marginal prices, based on typical billing, and using average prices produces nearly the same results.[25] The similarity may be due to the use of aggregated data. No unique marginal or average price exists for any state or region; therefore, the distinction between the two pricing systems may be obscured. Nevertheless, the average price is interpreted as a measure of the efficient level of the rate schedule for the particular consumer sector.

All variables are measured in constant dollars. There are economic and statistical reasons for this. Consumers make decisions in terms of their real consumption relative to their real income and relative to the real prices. If all money incomes and prices of goods and services were to double simultaneously, consumers would still spend the same proportion of their income on the good in question.[26] Further, the correct deflator should be used for personal income. The use of the consumer price index as the correct one can be defended on the grounds that personal income ought to be deflated by a price index measuring the amount of a good that can be bought in physical terms.[27] For these reasons the per capita personal income measure is deflated by the consumer price index and the price of electrical energy and the price of gas are deflated by the combined gas and electrical energy price index. While it would have been desirable to have separate indexes for electrical energy and for gas, they were not available. However, since the prices have moved over the period in roughly similar fashion, little bias is introduced by using the combined measure. Finally, while it would be desirable to have all price indexes on a regional level, such indexes do not exist so the national aggregate is used.

The income data present a problem in another way because they represent personal income instead of disposable personal income. Unfortunately, no estimates of regional disposable personal income exist over the period. One can approximate each region's disposable personal income using the ratio of United States disposable personal income to United States personal income and multiplying this ratio times each region's personal income. The assumption is that the relation for the United States is exactly representative of each region.[28] When one looks at the ratio of United States disposable personal income to United States personal income over the period 1947 to 1970, it varies only slightly. As a result, given the multiplicative nature of the model employed, the elasticity estimates would not change.[29] Parenthetically, if disposable personal income were used, the prediction problem would be compounded since it is not certain that this past ratio will remain unchanged in the future, and predicted levels of income are in terms of personal income.

In formally justifying the geometrically distributed lag model, it was mentioned in an earlier section that the equilibrium level of the dependent variable will not be attained until some time after the change in the independent variables has taken place. The desired demand y^*_{ijt} is described such that

$$y^*_{ijt} = f(PCPI_{jt}, P_{e_{ijt}}, P_{g_{ij(t-1)}}) \tag{2.3}$$

where $PCPI$ = per capita personal income,

Pe = the price of electrical energy, and

Pg = the price of gas.

Also i = ith sector,

j = jth region, and

t = tth year.

One then sees that this level of demand is reached only in conditions of long-run equilibrium. The ratio of current demand to demand in the previous period is assumed to be some power of the ratio of equilibrium demand to demand in the previous period:[30]

$$\frac{y_{ijt}}{y_{ij(t-1)}} = \left(\frac{y^*_{ijt}}{y_{ij(t-1)}} \right)^{\nu_i} \qquad 0 < \nu_i < 1 \tag{2.4}$$

Hence, actual demand, y_{ijt}, is given by:

$$y_{ijt} = (y^*_{ijt})^{\nu_i} \, (y_{ij(t-1)})^{(1-\nu_i)} \tag{2.5}$$

Transforming (2.5) and using an exact functional specification for (2.3) one gets (2.2). This is the reason for the term $y_{ij(t-1)}$ in the model. The essence of the term is that it captures not only the subjective factors such as tastes that influence the demand for electrical energy (assuming of course such factors are relatively stable from one period to the next), but it is also a normalizing term that allows one to take into account the different geographical sizes of regions.

The price of gas is lagged one period to take account of the delay in shifting from one energy source to another. When the price of gas changes, the effects are not felt until the following period when the consumer purchases new appliances or machinery. Before the actual results are presented, a note on the estimation procedure is provided. The estimates were obtained using both ordinary least squares and instrumental variables.[31] The values of the price elasticity of electrical energy for each sector for the instrumental variable estimator were consistently greater than one. These values are unreasonable since in the short run, the consumer for the most part can only vary the intensity of use of the existing stock of appliances and machinery and consequently the elasticity should be less than one.[32] Thus the ordinary least squares estimates are chosen as the more accurate estimation of the true parameter values.

The regression results for the estimated model for each sector are presented in Table 2-2, Table 2-3, and Table 2-4. In each case the fit of the model is good with the multiple correlation coefficient over 0.99. The only restrictions imposed were that for each sector the coefficient on the variable part of the gas coefficient be zero and that for the industrial sector, the variable part of the income coefficient be zero. In preliminary analyses,

Table 2-2
Residential Demand

Explanatory Factor[a]	*Parameter*	*Estimate*[b]
Lagged Demand	ϕ_1	0.88500 (0.01265)
Per Capita Personal Income	π_{11}	0.37639 (0.04610)
	δ_{11}	0.76527 (0.12240)
Price of Electrical Energy	π_{12}	−0.18461 (0.05216)
	δ_{12}	0.73607 (1.0114)
Price of Gas	π_{13}	0.04805 (0.01854)
	δ_{13}	0.00000 (...)
Region		
North East	A_{11}	0.81473
Mid Atlantic	A_{12}	0.94267
East North Central	A_{13}	0.97845
West North Central	A_{14}	0.92921
South Atlantic	A_{15}	0.96594
East South Central	A_{16}	0.83542
West South Central	A_{17}	0.96197
Mountain	A_{18}	0.81682
Pacific	A_{19}	0.87610

[a]Units of Measurement—Demand (millions of kWh)
—Income (thousand dollars per capita)
—Price of Electrical Energy (mills per kWh (deflated))
—Price of Gas (dollars per thousand therms (deflated))

[b]The values of the regional coefficients were obtained by collapsing the coefficients of the regional variables into the constant term.

each of these coefficients were not significant and therefore were omitted. The values in parentheses are the standard errors of the estimates.

Interpretation

One of the major conclusions from the empirical results is that the quantity demanded of electrical energy is about as responsive to price changes as to income changes for the residential sector but is generally less responsive to income changes than to price changes in the commercial and industrial sectors. This is not surprising in light of the fact that per capita income

Table 2-3
Commercial Demand

Explanatory Factor[a]	*Parameter*	*Estimate*[b]
Lagged Demand	ϕ_2	0.80984 (0.02814)
Per Capita Personal Income	π_{21}	0.13631 (0.13424)
	δ_{21}	0.43378 (0.27734)
Price of Electrical Energy	π_{22}	−0.47555 (0.15501)
	δ_{22}	5.8491 (4.2423)
Price of Gas	π_{23}	0.07729 (0.05282)
	δ_{23}	0.00000 (...)
Region		
North East	A_{21}	2.5234
Mid Atlantic	A_{22}	2.7070
East North Central	A_{23}	2.7330
West North Central	A_{24}	2.6048
South Atlantic	A_{25}	2.6048
East South Central	A_{26}	2.2696
West South Central	A_{27}	2.5737
Mountain	A_{28}	2.3710
Pacific	A_{29}	2.4836

[a]Units of Measurement—See Table 2-2
[b]See Table 2-2

really operates indirectly to influence the demand by the commercial and industrial sectors. The commercial and industrial components exhibit a derived demand for electrical energy. It is the demand for the output reflected through its price and the level of economic activity (i.e., effective demand) that determines the position of derived demand.[33] In the framework developed here then, per capita personal income is a proxy for the level of economic activity.

When attention is focused on the price elasticity of energy, an interesting phenomenon is noticed. Table 2-5, in conjunction with Tables 2-2 through 2-4, shows that for the residential and commercial sectors, the demand becomes increasingly elastic, i.e., more responsive to price changes, as the quantity increases. On the other hand, the industrial sector demand for electrical energy becomes increasingly inelastic. These results are not spurious. Not only are the signs insensitive to the model

Table 2-4
Industrial Demand

Explanatory Factor[a]	*Parameter*	*Estimate*[b]
Lagged Demand	ϕ_3	0.86403 (0.02891)
Per Capita Personal Income	π_{31}	0.12486 (0.06113)
	δ_{31}	0.00000 (...)
Price of Electrical Energy	π_{32}	−0.64432 (0.15885)
	δ_{32}	−3.8170 (1.4800)
Price of Gas	π_{33}	0.07152 (0.03602)
	δ_{33}	0.00000 (...)
Region		
North East	A_{31}	2.8930
Mid Atlantic	A_{32}	3.0047
East North Central	A_{33}	3.0750
West North Central	A_{34}	2.9812
South Atlantic	A_{35}	3.0199
East South Central	A_{36}	2.9959
West South Central	A_{37}	3.0109
Mountain	A_{38}	2.8153
Pacific	A_{39}	2.8997

[a]Units of Measurement—See Table 2-2
[b]See Table 2-2

specification,[34] but also the relative magnitudes of the coefficients did not change with alternate specifications.

Of the studies estimating the of demand for elasticity electrical energy in the residential sector, the ones by Mount, Chapman, and Tyrrell[35] and by Fisher and Kaysen[36] lend solid support for the results here even though both studies look at demand on a more disaggregated state basis. Other studies use different model specifications and comparison is not justified.[37] The study of Fisher and Kaysen was the first extensive look at the demand for electrical energy in the United States. Their analysis is subject to errors at various points. Among other things, as noted by Wilson,[38] their data are of uncertain quality. They use state-wide data, and state and market boundaries do not coincide. The variables they use are all time-dominated, resulting in a high degree of correlation over time. This means that nothing about causal relationships is revealed.

Table 2-5
Price Elasticities Evaluated at 1970 Electrical Energy Prices
(Price Level is in Parenthesis)[a]

Region	*Residential Sector*	*Commercial Sector*	*Industrial Sector*
1. North East	−0.21296 (25.967)	−0.71811 (24.114)	−0.37760 (14.311)
2. Mid Atlantic	−0.21297 (25.959)	−0.71184 (24.141)	−0.31241 (11.500)
3. East North Central	−0.21635 (23.194)	−0.73893 (22.208)	−0.29223 (10.841)
4. West North Central	−0.21508 (24.159)	−0.73876 (22.222)	−0.34162 (12.610)
5. South Atlantic	−0.22285 (19.251)	−0.78371 (18.981)	−0.24688 (9.6040)
6. East South Central	−0.23712 (21.222)	−0.81895 (18.095)	−0.09864 (6.9950)
7. West South Central	−0.21929 (21.222)	−0.79879 (18.095)	−0.18030 (8.2260)
8. Mountain	−0.21900 (21.403)	−0.79744 (18.171)	−0.17384 (8.1130)
9. Pacific	−0.22774 (17.065)	−0.83110 (16.451)	−0.06930 (6.6380)

[a]The prices are in average mills per kWh in 1970 dollars.

Many of these problems were corrected in the work of Mount, Chapman, and Tyrrell, and it is this work that is used as the point of reference with which the results obtained here are compared. The comparison is not only for the residential sector but also for the industrial sector. Their data are more reliable and their methodology, the pooling of cross-section and time-series observations, is more appropriate.

For the residential sector, Mount, Chapman, and Tyrrell get an estimated elasticity of −0.14. They use, in addition to the variables employed in this study, population, and prices of appliances, and they deflate all money values by the consumer price index. As noted above this deflator is not especially appropriate when the price index for gas and electrical energy is available. Further, the use of both population and income as exogenous variables leaves one with an uneasy feeling. The two series are so highly correlated even when logarithmic values are used that the standard errors become enormous, and thus one seldom finds both variables significant in any regression equation.[39] Technically, multicollinearity between two variables discourages inclusion of both of them. This reservation is borne out in their study in that income is not significant in explaining the demand for electrical energy though they report and continue to use the estimate.

These weaknesses might not explain the total difference between the results of Mount, Chapman, and Tyrrell and this study. It is likely that some of the variation is due to the aggregation problem.[40] Specifically, in practice one does not know enough about micro behavior to be able to specify micro equations perfectly. Hence, empirically estimated micro relations should not be assumed to be perfectly specified.[41] Aggregation of the economic variables involved can reduce these specification errors not only when aggregating from the individual consumer units to the state but also when aggregating from the state to the regional level. Further, accurately measuring the variables presents some statistical problems.[42] One would anticipate a greater measurement error the more refined the unit under consideration. For example, there is more error in measuring state per capita income than in measuring regional income because a person can live in one state and work in another with the resulting income accounts allocation incorrect. Also since a utility company supplies power to states other than the one in which it is located, the statistical allocation of the revenues might be improper.

Summarily, all of the problems taken together can be significant enough to explain the difference in the estimated elasticity between the value reported here and the result of Mount, Chapman, and Tyrrell.

It is interesting to conjecture why the price elasticity in the residential sector decreases as the price level increases. It can be seen from Table 2-6 that the regions that have a higher average use per customer for the most part also have a high elasticity. Beyond the basic electrical energy usage, the higher average in some regions indicates a greater frequency of the use of items such as electric clothes dryers, electric water heaters, space heaters, electric stoves, color television sets, and so on. With an increase in the price of electrical energy, the regions possessing more of these luxuries have the potential of reducing the intensity of use of these appliances and therefore can respond more strongly to a price increase. Again, the high average use regions, since they own more electric appliances per household,[43] would be able to decrease their electrical energy consumption levels much farther and yet not be deprived of the function of their appliances as price rises.

The results for the commercial sector are more difficult to interpret. Many of the comments made concerning the residential sector's demand for electrical energy are applicable here because in both sectors electrical energy is a final good. However for the commercial sector some of the electrical energy consumed is as an intermediate good, while this is not the case for the residential sector. Commerical electrical energy consumption

Table 2-6
Average Use of Electrical Energy by a Residential Consumer in 1971

Region	*Average (kWh)*
1. North East	5888.3
2. Mid Atlantic	5529.2
3. East North Central	6528.5
4. West North Central	6828.8
5. South Atlantic	8700.0
6. East South Central	10917.3
7. West South Central	8286.8
8. Mountain	6925.8
9. Pacific	7723.7

Source: Edison Electric Institute, *Statistical Yearbook of the Electric Utility Industry for 1971,* New York.

includes the demands of the following users: wholesale and retail trade, transportation (except railroads), communication, utilities (except electric), finance, real estate, insurance, services, and construction. The fact that commercial electrical energy consumption includes the demands of widely differing types of users makes it difficult to deal with as an aggregated whole. The technological peculiarities of the communications, utilities, and construction segments are responsible for important components of their demand. The problem may be less severe for trade, finance, real estate, insurance, and services.[44]

Although the commercial sector is a substantial and growing consumer of electrical energy, little information is available on its consumption categories. The discussion of air conditioning makes reference to the commercial sector. Generally, office buildings, stores and so on are nearly (80-90%) saturated with air conditioning, whereas schools represent a virtually untapped (10%) market. (Schools fall within the commercial sector). With regard to the use of electrical energy for space heating, electric heat is steadily penetrating areas of the commercial market formerly dominated by fossil fuels.[45]

The real problem with explaining the price elasticity estimates for the commercial sector is how to account for such an absolutely much larger value than that of the residential sector or of the industrial sector. An increasing proportion of commercial establishments have electric heating and central air conditioning. The average usage per square foot appears to be increasing. It seems that the bulk of the growth of electrical energy is due to increased usage per square foot.[46] One can see that even more than for the residential sector, the commercial sector can vary the intensity of its usage. This is in fact the thrust of the considerations by Doctor, et al., when they observe that the amount of electrical energy potentially saved by reducing equipment usage hours in the commercial sector is quantitatively greater than that for the residential sector even though the residential sector uses a larger proportion of electrical energy.[47]

The feature that the commercial sector possesses that is absent from the residential sector is the ability to change energy sources in a relatively short period of time. It becomes economically feasible when price increases become substantial for elements in the commercial sector to change either to coal, oil, or gas as substitutes for electrical energy.

These two factors then, the reduction in intensity of use and changing to alternative fuel sources, can account for the relatively large price elasticity in the commercial sector. Additionally, the same structure of average energy use across regions is present for the commercial sector as was observed for the residential sector indicating the viability of the varying intensity hypothesis.

After the residential sector, the industrial sector has been the most widely studied with regard to its demand for electrical energy. The industrial sector includes manufacturing, mining, and agriculture. Electrical energy use in this sector is controlled by the technical requirements of production, particularly those relating to mechanical functions or electrochemical reactions. It is these "process uses" of electrical energy that dominate its use in industry.[48] Given this consideration, Fisher and Kaysen and more recently Anderson[49] have divided the elasticity into two separate components. The fixed component, which is relatively insensitive to price changes, reflects the technical requirements. This is expressly manifested through locational decisions of industries. Those with high electrical energy requirements have based their locational decisions on the availability of cheap power. Since geographical patterns in electrical energy tend to be fairly constant over time, current electrical energy price is likely to be highly correlated over regions with the price that determined such decisions and hence with capacity output.

The variable component of the elasticity reflects the intensity of use of electrical energy not for the industrial process itself but for the support of the process in the form of lighting, air conditioning and so on. As the price of the input factors rise (which results in some reduction of use of the factors), the output price rises reducing the quantity of output demanded, further reducing the quantity of the input factor demanded, magnifying the response to the initial price change. One of the input factors is electrical energy. As was the case for the commercial and the residential sectors, the industrial sector has the ability to vary the intensity of use of electrical energy. However, unlike the commercial sector, it technologically does not have much opportunity to switch to alternative energy sources.[50]

As a result of these considerations, one would expect first, a relatively inelastic demand for electrical energy and second, an increasing inelasticity of demand as the industrial sector consumes a greater quantity of and becomes more dependent on electrical energy and consequently less responsive to electrical energy price changes. The expectations are borne out by the results in Table 2-4 and Table 2-5.

Once again with the work of Mount, Chapman, and Tyrrell[51] as the reference point, the elasticity values for the industrial sector obtained here are slightly larger than their estimates. They get an estimated elasticity of −0.25. In trying to reconcile the differences between their results and the ones presented here, the comments made above for the residential sector are again appropriate and need not be repeated. A reconciliation of the disparity can be cast totally in terms of those considerations.

As a final note, a look at the relative responsiveness of the three sectors indicates that the commercial sector is the most responsive to price changes even though it is still price inelastic. This, a priori, is expected because the residential consumers have adjusted to a particular life style and are reluctant to relinquish it, while the industrial consumer is restricted technologically by its facilities and production methods to a greater extent than the commercial consumer. To posit an explanation of the greater responsiveness to price changes by the industrial sector than by the residential sector would be tenuous. Suffice it to say that demand responds relatively slowly to changes in the causal factors and consequently any adaptation of present life style or of existing facilities and production processes to the change will also be gradual.

3 Future Demand for Electrical Energy

As was noted in chapter 2, an indirect approach must be used to obtain the requisite estimates of linear demand functions for electrical energy in the United States. Specifically, it has been decided that first determining the price elasticity and then deriving fixed point estimates of demand is a more appropriate procedure than others available because of the identification and functional form specification problems.

The methodology adopted for demand projections in this study is that discussed by Theil[1] and consists mainly of using the coefficients of the demand model determined in chapter 2, the likely changes in per capita personal income, the likely changes in the price of electrical energy and the likely changes in the price of gas over the period in arriving at a projected quantity demanded. All of the expected changes have been borrowed from other sources. This quantity demand figure is then combined with the expected price level of electrical energy to determine the linear price-quantity relationship.

Background[2]

Demand forecast methodology involves the analytical approach and techniques used to make electrical energy forecasts. A general discussion on problems in forecasting is contained elsewhere[3] and need not be summarized here. The appropriateness of methodology depends on forecast objectives: a particular methodology may be capable of dealing with one concept but it may be incapable of dealing with another. Likewise the interpretations that can be given to forecast results depend on the methods used to obtain them. Regardless of how forecasts are labeled, they cannot be given interpretations that go beyond the limitations imposed by the methods used to derive them. For example, an analysis and projection of electrical energy consumption that fails to deal with price cannot be interpreted as a price-quantity demand relationship.

Two basic forms of statistical projection techniques have been employed in most of the electrical energy forecasts.[4] Time trend analysis calculates historical trends in electrical energy consumption by determining a relationship between electrical energy consumption and time. By the very nature of time trend analysis, projections of its calculated trends will yield accurate forecasts if the projected historical relationship continues. Thus, time trend forecasts are based on an assumption that economic forces that have produced a certain trend in electrical energy consumption in the past will continue to produce energy consumption levels with the same trend in the future. Ultimately, however, it is economic factors that can affect the future trend in energy consumption and, thus, the accuracy of the forecasting relationship upon which time trend projections are based. The accuracy of this observation can be supported by the capacity shortages that have existed particularly in the Northeast since 1965. By not taking sufficient account of the economic factors involved, the Federal Power Commission and the individual utility companies in the region underestimated demand.

Multiple regression analysis calculates the historical trends in the relationship between electrical energy consumption and various economic variables and uses them as forecasting relationships to project future electrical energy consumption. By the very nature of multiple regression analysis, its projections will be accurate if forecasting relationships (the coefficients on the demand model) continue to hold in the future and if assumptions about the future level of economic variables are accurate.

While the forecasting relationship calculated by regression analysis may be good for predictive purposes, they do not necessarily represent causal relationships. For example, electrical energy consumption is highly correlated with population, so this variable might be valuable in making energy projections. It does not, however, necessarily cause electrical energy consumption to be at a certain level nor is it necessarily related economically to electrical energy consumption, and hence the regression forecasts would have to be interpreted accordingly.

Finally, judgment is employed in forecasting in a variety of ways. Even when time trend or multiple regression analyses are used mechanically to calculate and project historical trends, judgment is used in choosing the source of data, the time period of the data, and the type of forecasting relationship (exponential in this study) to be fitted to the data. Regardless of judgment is used, it must accurately account for the influence of what it considers or forecasts with the realization that these considerations or forecasts are subject to error.

Projection Techniques

The forecasting methodology employed is a combination of the techniques discussed in the preceding section. By incorporating the lagged endogenous term in the demand model as one of the predetermined variables, one is capturing the relationship between electrical energy consumption and time. Because of the strong tendency of the electrical energy time series to maintain its rate of change, it is important to take account of this relation. A look at the empirical results section of chapter 2 will indicate the theoretical derivation of this accomplishment.

Suppose one wants to predict the level of the electrical energy demand next year by a particular sector in a specific region. The theory is that the current period's demand is some function of the current period's per capita personal income and price of electrical energy and the last period's price of gas. A sample of T annual observations has been used to get an estimate of the exact functional relationship among variables. The task is to predict $y_{ij(T+1)}$, which according to equation (2.1) is determined by

$$y_{ij(T+1)} = A_{ij} y_{ijT}^{\phi i} V_{1ij(T+1)}^{\pi 1i} \ldots V_{nij(T+1)}^{\pi ni} e^{\delta 1i/V_{1ij(T+1)}} \ldots e^{\delta ni/V_{nij(T+1)}} e^{\epsilon_{ij(T+1)}} \quad (3.1)$$

One must take the $V_{kij(T+1)}$'s as given. That is, a conditional forecast of next year's level of electrical energy demand will be formulated given a specified level of the independent variables next period. This implies that the level of these variables are known, and given that the parameters in the equation are not known exactly, the least squares estimates of chapter 2 must be employed. Further, since the $\epsilon_{ij(T+1)}$ is unknown, it is supposed that the T + 1 disturbances, $\epsilon_{ij1}, \ldots, \epsilon_{ij(T+1)}$ are all independent random variables with zero mean and variance σ^2. This condition implies that $\epsilon_{ij(T+1)}$ is independent of all previous disturbances. One can therefore have no hope of doing better than predicting $\epsilon_{ij(T+1)}$ by its expectation, which is zero.

Note that this is a conditional point prediction: One has for each of the independent variables a number that is given, for the parameters ϕ, $\pi_1, \ldots, \pi_n, \delta_1, \ldots, \delta_n$ point estimates that are computed from data referring to T years in the past, and for their product also a single number.[6] This process can be repeated to obtain predictions of the level of the electrical energy demand in period $T+2, T+3, \ldots, T+K$. The same remarks that were made when projecting the demand for period $T+1$ hold for these future periods.[7]

The levels of the independent variable are not known beforehand. It is thus necessary to predict these levels, after which the prediction is substituted into equation (3.1) to obtain a forecast of $y_{ij(T+1)}$. This forecast obviously ceases to be unconditional when no fixed a priori values of the independent variables are taken as given. It is also obvious that the errors on predicting $V_{kij(T+1)}$ will play a role when looking at the variance of the error in predicting $y_{ij(T+1)}$.[8]

It was assumed when making the estimates in the regression analysis that the variables have no measurement error, which might not be completely realistic. If the independent variables are subject to such errors, the analysis is more complicated. The problem of measurement errors in general is important for the evaluation of predictions. Recognizing the existence of a true value, an observed value, and a point prediction, one can discuss the concept of observed prediction error. The sum and substance of the consideration is that the observed prediction error variance underestimates the true quality of the forecast. Measurement errors do play a disturbing role in the evaluation of predictions.[9]

Projecting Growth to 1990

In this section independent projections of regional population and total personal income, and the price of electrical energy and the price of gas, together with the quantitative estimates of the parameters of the demand model, are used to relate explicitly electrical energy demand projections to assumptions about causal factors.[10]

The source of estimates of regional per capita personal income was the estimates of regional population and total regional income in a study prepared by the Bureau of Economic Analysis (BEA) of the Department of Commerce.[11] Regional per capita personal income is obtained by dividing total personal income in a region by population. Area population changes are projected by the BEA as a function of changes in area employment. Because projected employment changes are reconciled with projected changes in earnings of employees, and because earnings form the bulk of personal income, there is a strong correlation between changes in population and those in income. The projected population movements are generally in line with past trends with only New England and the Mountain regions the significant exceptions.[12]

Personal income projections indicate that the Pacific, East South Central, West South Central, and South Atlantic regions will continue to increase their share of the nation's personal income. However, their share will grow at rates only about one-third as fast as in the 1950-1970 period. The continued increase is largely because of continued rapid growth in manufacturing in most states of these regions. In the two southern regions, a "catch-up" expansion in service industries, representing a maturing of the economic structure is another factor. The projections show continued down trends in the share of the nations's income going to the Middle Atlantic, East North Central, and West North Central regions. The Middle Atlantic decline is a reflection of both the age and the economic maturity of the region and it is not possible to single out one or two industries as responsible. The East North Central region has a large industrial capacity with emphasis on durable goods production. There has been a gradual shift in the share of durable goods industries away from this region leaving

Table 3-1
Per Capita Income Percent Change by Region, 1971-1980 and 1981-1990

Region	*Percent Change 1971-1980*	*Percent Change 1981-1990*
1. New England	3.31%	2.82%
2. Middle Atlantic	3.33	2.80
3. East North Central	3.53	2.83
4. West North Central	3.67	3.09
5. South Atlantic	3.75	3.16
6. East South Central	4.33	3.39
7. West South Central	3.79	3.16
8. Mountain	3.72	3.07
9. Pacific	3.48	2.72

excess labor and plant capacity. The dominant role of agriculture in the West North Central region is the sole explanation of the projected decline there.[13]

These population and income projections combine to yield the per capita personal income growth rates represented in Table 3-1. The values are the rates of increase annually for the period 1971-1980 and 1981-1990 for each region.

There is wide variation in analyses of future cost increases. For gas, it has been argued that "past commissions have placed primary emphasis on maintaining the lowest possible gas price, with little attention being given to incentives needed to insure continued adequate reserves of proven natural gas in the ground."[14] As the President fully recognizes in his 1973 Energy Message, the price paid to producers must increase if there is to be the needed incentive for increasing supply and reducing inefficient usage, and he suggests that gas should no longer be subject to price regulation at the well head. At the same time, the consumer must be protected against precipitous cost increases.[15] In view of these considerations, the Federal Power Commission has made projections of the average price increase most likely to occur as well as a maximum and minimum expected increase. It is the median projection that will be used, and it is simply assumed that the price of gas in each sector of each region will roughly follow the national trend. This means an average 2.675 percent increase in 1971, a 3.6 percent increase in 1972, a 2.4 percent increase in each of the years from 1973 to 1980, and a 4.2 percent increase in each of the years from 1981 to 1990 will persist in each sector across regions.[16]

Present events have eliminated the hope that the utility industry can continue supplying electrical energy reliably and economically. Environmentalists insist on stringent requirements by 1975 as opposed to the original target of 1977. In other cases utilities have been required to install antipollution devices to reduce the stack gas emissions. Projects have been barred completely on the premise that a project cannot be permitted to degrade appreciably the quality of the environment. Such decisions have imposed delays on projects and have forced recourse to less economical alternatives. Additionally, delays preventing construction and licensing of planned nuclear generating plants are forcing and will continue to force the greater use of all plants burning more costly fuel.[17]

These considerations, superimposed on rising construction costs, have resulted in rising power rates and an expected continued rise. Under current restraints, the most favorable prognosis coming from the electrical energy industry itself now sees a continuing rise in the cost of electrical energy in the residential sector until 1985, at which point it should level off. The actual projection can be found in Table 3-2.[18] Observe that the projected increase in prices is slightly higher than the 19 percent increase expected by the Federal Power Commission.[19] It is simply argued that the projection of the industry is more recent (1973 versus 1969 for the FPC) and apparently relies on some type of econometric model and consequently is more respectable. Further, the projection coincides nicely with that shown independently by Nordhaus.[20]

Heretofore, price changes in one sector have paralleled changes in the remaining sectors. It is assumed this will continue to be the case in the future. Additionally, it is assumed that regional price changes will behave exactly as the national average. This assumption is necessitated because regional projections do not exist.

It should be noted that projections selected have been subjectively chosen. Recall the point raised in the first section of this chapter that judgment is employed when forecasting in choosing the source of data and the time period. While the actual problem specification depends heavily on the forecasted relationships (the temporal aspect of the model), some sensitivity analysis will be performed to see the effects of possible errors in judgment.[21]

For the purpose at hand, it is not necessary to report all of the projections for the years 1975, 1980, 1985, and 1990 for each sector in each region. The magnitude of the change can be felt by observation of a summary in Table 3-3 of the percentage change between the base period 1970 and 1990. The predictions in each region for the commercial sector are the combined result of a decline in the quantity of electrical energy demanded until about 1985 and then an increase. This can be explained in part by the calculation of the elasticity of the price of electrical energy, which reflects the facility with which the commercial sector can respond to price changes by shifting to alternative energy sources. This is discussed more completely in chapter 2. It is interesting to observe that the commercial sector is not expected to

Table 3-2
Residential Price Increase for Electrical Energy, 1971-1990

Year	*Percent Increase from 1970*
1971	4.2%
1972	9.0
1973	12.9
1974	15.2
1975	17.6
1976	20.0
1977	22.4
1978	23.8
1979	24.8
1980	25.7
1981	26.0
1982	26.3
1983	26.6
1984	26.9
1985-1990	27.1

Source: L. Olmsted, "24th Annual Electrical Energy Forecast," *Electrical World*, September 15, 1973.

get back to the level of electrical energy utilization that existed in 1970 in some regions.

Linear Demand Functions

Once price and quantity projections are available, it is a short move to get the requisite linear demand relations. The procedure is straightforward and is briefly outlined in what follows. First compute the price elasticity for a specific sector in a specific region for each of the periods 1970, 1975, 1980, 1985 and 1990. (Recall from chapter 2 that working with a variable elasticity model entails a different elasticity for each price level.) Call η_{ijt} the price elasticity for any given period.

The form of the demand function can be either

$$y_{ijt} = \alpha_{ijt} - \beta_{ijt} Pe_{ijt} \tag{3.2}$$

or

$$Pe_{ijt} = \lambda_{ijt} - \omega_{ijt} y_{ijt} \tag{3.2a}$$

Table 3-3
Percentage Change in Electrical Energy Use by Region and Sector, 1970-1990

Region	*Residential Sector*	*Commercial Sector*	*Industrial Sector*
1. New England	201.9%	8.7%	65.9%
2. Middle Atlantic	209.8	−21.5	36.7
3. East North Central	187.7	−10.4	47.6
4. West North Central	217.4	5.1	46.7
5. South Atlantic	213.1	− 9.4	78.7
6. East South Central	132.1	−29.4	114.9
7. West South Central	218.8	0.7	96.8
8. Mountain	184.1	−27.4	56.0
9. Pacific	197.2	−27.6	59.9

for $i =$ sector (1 = residential, 2 = commercial, and 3 = industrial),
$j =$ region (i = 1, 2, . . . , 9),
$t =$ period (1 = 1970, 2 = 1975, 3 = 1980, 4 = 1985, and 5 = 1990),
$Pe =$ price, and
$y =$ quantity of electrical energy demanded.

The elasticity is defined as

$$\frac{\partial y_{ijt}}{\partial Pe_{ijt}}\left(\frac{Pe^{o}_{ijt}}{y^{o}_{ijt}}\right) = \eta_{ijt} \tag{3.3}$$

so that, using equation (3.2), one gets

$$\beta_{ijt} = -\eta_{ijt}\left(\frac{y^{o}_{ijt}}{Pe^{o}_{ijt}}\right) \tag{3.4}$$

where y^{o}_{ijt} and Pe^{o}_{jt} are the values of price and quantity that exist or are expected to exist for any i, j, t. (The superscript denotes that the value must be known before β_{ijt} can be computed.)

Once the β_{ijt}'s are known the α_{ijt}'s can be computed. The values are just

$$\alpha_{ijt} = y^{o}_{ijt} + \beta_{ijt}Pe^{o}_{ijt} \tag{3.5}$$

The numerical results can be found in tables 3-4 through 3-6. The value of λ_{ijt} and ω_{ijt} can be obtained by solving equation (3.2a) for Pe_{ijt}.

Now that the demand curves have been secured, one can proceed to other considerations, but not before taking a moment to reflect on these past two chapters. The forecasts have been based on data of historical electrical energy consumption and an assumption that fuel and energy

Table 3-4
Linear Demand Coefficients for the Residential Sector

Region	*Year*	α_{1jt}	β_{1jt}
1. New England	1970	25,350.8	171.4
	1975	34,314.7	194.0
	1980	43,418.1	228.2
	1985	56,640.4	294.1
	1990	76,140.8	395.3
2. Middle Atlantic	1970	72,424.9	489.8
	1975	98,623.1	557.8
	1980	125,754.1	661.3
	1985	165,178.6	858.0
	1990	223,226.6	1,159.5
3. East North Central	1970	96,926.9	743.3
	1975	127,820.0	818.3
	1980	159,864.3	951.0
	1985	207,246.9	1,217.6
	1990	277,177.8	1,629.1
4. West North Central	1970	42,939.6	314.6
	1975	59,565.1	364.5
	1980	76,187.2	433.4
	1985	100,118.8	562.5
	1990	135,549.2	761.6
5. South Atlantic	1970	99,653.3	943.3
	1975	137,612.9	1,084.2
	1980	175,012.3	1,279.8
	1985	229,210.7	1,655.1
	1990	309,961.7	2,238.2
6. East South Central	1970	54,170.8	740.6
	1975	65,470.0	740.5
	1980	76,520.9	801.5
	1985	95,133.4	983.5
	1990	124,569.4	1,287.9
7. West South Central	1970	58,522.5	496.0
	1975	82,453.0	582.5
	1980	105,471.1	893.3
	1990	185,413.3	1,201.5
8. Mountain	1970	20,695.0	173.7
	1975	27,325.1	191.2
	1980	33,924.2	220.5
	1985	43,738.5	280.8
	1990	58,440.5	375.1
9. Pacific	1970	76,003.4	826.2
	1975	101,909.7	919.9
	1980	128,626.0	1,076.8
	1985	167,467.2	1,384.3
	1990	224,193.4	1,853.1

Table 3-5
Linear Demand Coefficients for the Commercial Sector

Region	*Year*	α_{2ij}	β_{2ij}
1. New England	1970	25,158.3	436.1
	1975	28,689.1	410.1
	1980	25,662.7	339.2
	1985	25,135.1	327.8
	1990	26,528.2	346.0
2. Middle Atlantic	1970	83,291.1	1,441.7
	1975	76,282.3	1,088.9
	1980	63,346.8	836.1
	1985	60,543.5	788.6
	1990	63,419.0	826.1
3. East North Central	1970	93,747.3	1,793.8
	1975	94,683.2	1,491.9
	1980	80,713.8	1,175.3
	1985	77,601.3	1,115.0
	1990	81,301.2	1,168.2
4. West North Central	1970	37,219.9	711.6
	1975	41,976.2	660.9
	1980	37,047.2	539.1
	1985	35,995.7	516.8
	1990	37,840.7	543.3
5. South Atlantic	1970	89,820.3	2,079.1
	1975	93,092.5	1,770.0
	1980	78,720.7	1,381.7
	1985	75,111.5	1,300.7
	1990	78,410.1	1,357.8
6. East South Central	1970	25,736.3	680.3
	1975	23,182.7	502.5
	1980	18,331.9	366.5
	1985	16,954.7	334.4
	1990	17,433.9	343.9
7. West South Central	1970	64,544.3	1,584.0
	1975	72,481.1	1,459.9
	1980	62,563.9	1,163.0
	1985	59,909.8	1,098.6
	1990	62,474.8	1,145.7
8. Mountain	1970	33,013.6	806.0
	1975	29,698.8	595.2
	1980	23,812.6	440.4
	1985	22,271.6	406.4
	1990	23,065.6	420.8
9. Pacific	1970	101,717.4	2,806.4
	1975	91,020.3	2,058.1
	1980	72,721.0	1,516.5
	1985	68,065.9	1,400.2
	1990	70,617.6	1,452.7

Table 3-6
Linear Demand Coefficients for the Industrial Sector

Region	*Year*	α_{3jt}	β_{3jt}
1. New England	1970	25,018.6	479.2
	1975	32,061.5	561.1
	1980	34,295.5	575.2
	1985	37,693.5	627.5
	1990	43,228.2	719.7
2. Middle Atlantic	1970	106,097.6	2,196.1
	1975	120,549.2	2,369.4
	1980	124,039.7	2,363.9
	1985	134,276.3	2,544.5
	1990	152,888.6	2,897.2
3. East North Central	1970	159,454.7	3,326.2
	1975	187,296.1	3,767.5
	1980	197,609.3	3,871.3
	1985	217,069.1	4,231.3
	1990	249,090.4	4,855.5
4. West North Central	1970	41,191.9	831.8
	1975	48,358.9	909.7
	1980	50,396.9	914.0
	1985	55,108.5	993.0
	1990	63,356.4	1,141.6
5. South Atlantic	1970	97,138.3	2,002.6
	1975	124,136.3	2,577.5
	1980	138,667.6	2,837.8
	1985	157,851.6	3,220.1
	1990	185,391.7	3,781.9
6. East South Central	1970	84,168.3	1,080.4
	1975	114,069.8	1,918.8
	1980	137,904.9	2,724.5
	1985	165,327.6	3,291.2
	1990	200,060.7	3,982.6
7. West South Central	1970	74,946.9	1,391.8
	1975	99,612.3	2,057.9
	1980	115,623.8	2,413.0
	1985	134,590.8	2,810.0
	1990	159,868.0	3,337.8
8. Mountain	1970	28,509.1	520.4
	1975	33,426.4	687.8
	1980	36,552.1	762.1
	1985	41,291.3	861.6
	1990	48,268.5	1,007.2
9. Pacific	1970	82,464.2	805.1
	1975	97,467.3	1,679.4
	1980	109,714.4	2,070.5
	1985	125,600.8	2,397.7
	1990	146,963.8	2,805.5

supply availabilities will be restricted in the future conditional on price adjustments. Projections based on past trends of actual energy consumption can be interpreted as forecasts of what future consumption will be. If supply and demand forces have interacted in the past in such a way as to produce a trend in energy consumption, they may very likely produce consumption levels that will follow the same trend in the future. With no reason to believe that future consumption will vary one way or the other from its historical trend, that trend becomes a basis for forecasting future electrical energy consumption. Consumption levels are determined by factors of both supply and demand. Forecasts of energy consumption do not necessarily examine these individual factors, but they do forecast what their net effect will be—a particular energy consumption level.

The exact consumption interpretation that is appropriate for projected energy consumption trends depends on both assumptions and actual anticipations about future energy availabilities. The study has assumed a conditionally restricted supply availability by introducing through the expected change in the level of the price of electrical energy the anticipated supply constraints and thus fully realizes that supply does influence the quantity consumed. To the extent to which the price movement projection is inaccurate however, the forecast will be unreliable.

Summarily, actual consumption levels are determined by factors of both supply and demand: simple regression analysis projections of past trends of energy consumption are not able to analyze factors of price, income, technology, or government policies as they relate to demand. It was essential to include the other factors when projecting future demand because one must consider the traditional price-quantity demand relationship, the desires and preferences for electrical energy, and the economic factors that influence the derived demand for electrical energy as a factor of production or as an element of a joint consumption item.

4 Transmission, Distribution, and Supply Considerations

Another basic assumption of the economic environment of the intertemporal-spatial price equilibrium model is that the supply function and interregional transmission and distribution costs for electrical energy are known. The first portion of the chapter looks at transmission and distribution costs, while the latter portion considers the supply relation.

Transmission Costs

Figure 4-1 shows the average and marginal costs for transmitting alternative amounts of electrical energy one mile. Each of the curves is defined as the envelope for the various voltages of transmission lines which, given present and expected technology over the next 20 years, could be used. For example, the average cost curve in figure 4-1 is drawn as the envelope for a number of short-run average cost curves, for each voltage line. Curve *M* might be the average cost relationship with a 230-kilovolt (kv) line, *N* with a 345-kv line, and *Z* with a 765-kv line. The point where curve *M*, *N*, . . ., *Z* touches the envelope determines a certain optimal load factor for both the individual curve and its envelope.[1] Average cost per mile is assumed to fall until an absolute physical capacity (*K*) is reached.[2] At capacity, cost equals the constant marginal cost.

The transmission activity is not perfectly divisible—to transmit one kilowatt requires that all the costs of constructing the minimum size transmission line be incurred. Additionally, some of the fixed cost of building a transmission line is independent of the line voltage. For example, one needs a right of way for a transmission line whether a 230-kv or a 500-kv line is being constructed. These features then—indivisibility and economies of scale in transmission—suggest the long-run curve pictured in Figure 4-1.

A cost function (C_{ij}) that captures both scale economies and indivisibilities is:

$$C_{ij} = ax_{ij} + bs_{ij} \tag{4.1}$$

($s_{ij} = 1, x_{ij} > 0; s_{ij} = 0, x_{ij} = 0$), where *b* represents the fixed cost necessary to transmit from region *i* to region *j* and *a* is the marginal cost for each kilowatt transmitted.[3] s_{ij} shows that where there is no flow, the fixed cost is zero and when the flow becomes positive, all of the fixed cost is incurred.

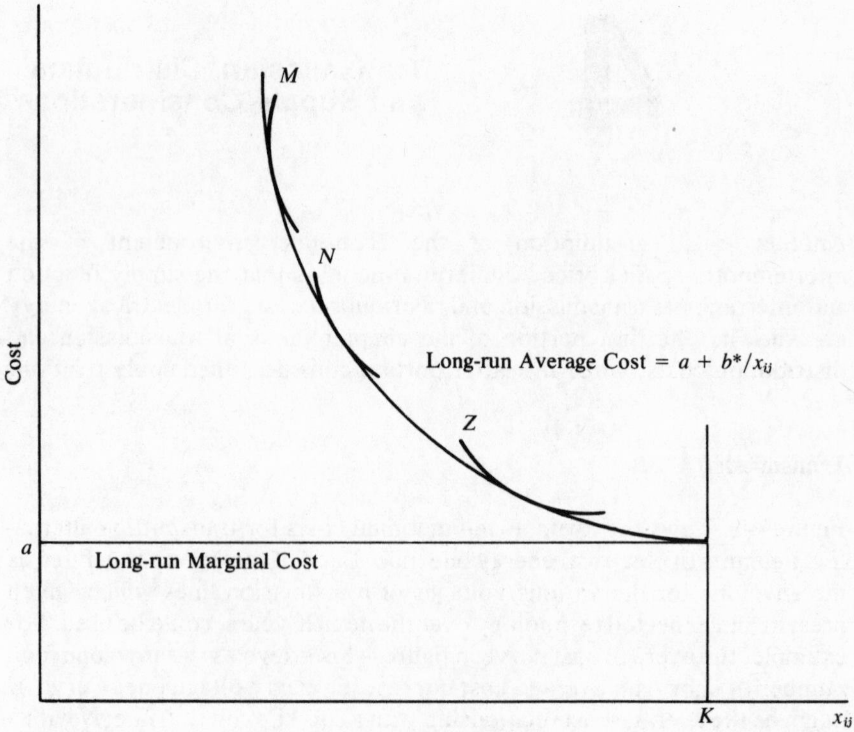

Figure 4-1. Average and Marginal Costs of Transmission per Mile

The assumption of a constant marginal cost, a, is somewhat arbitrary since the marginal cost of transmitting electrical energy might in fact fall with larger transmission lines if there is a saving on labor or fuel cost. Nevertheless, a simplification is needed to develop the model and the empirical fit of this functional specification (see the following section) is good.

The per mile transmission cost (C_{ij}) has to be multiplied by the distance between region i and region j (d_{ij}) to obtain the total cost of transmitting from i to j. Specifically, the total transmission cost is

$$d_{ij}C_{ij} = ad_{ij}x_{ij} + bd_{ij}s_{ij} \tag{4.2}$$

If one were to attempt to minimize an objective function with C_{ij} contained in it (which will be undertaken later), severe computational problems would be encountered. The total cost function is not convex between zero and one unit of transmission. At a zero flow, no fixed cost is incurred. To transmit just a single kilowatt, the entire fixed cost bd_{ij} must be incurred. Nonconvexities cannot be handled by quadratic programming.

The fixed charge problem is essentially ignored, with the transmission cost that will appear in the objective function being only the long-run marginal cost = $ad_{ij}x_{ij}$. How might one justify the omission of a fixed cost and argue that still a correct solution will obtain? The answer rests on two points: one intuitive and one empirical. If one were considering a highly disaggregated model with a large number of regions (say 100 or more), then ignoring fixed cost would see a potential for a tremendous number of flows. However, a larger transmission line with a lower average cost serving several regions might reduce cost. In the model employed, the level of aggregation is so high that the size of most flows expected are those that could be carried only on the larger transmission lines. Savings could not be encountered by letting a single line serve several regions. Consequently a linear approximation in a highly aggregate model need not necessarily be misleading.

Secondly, ignoring the fixed cost will lead to an incorrect solution to the nonlinear problem if this cost is of significant size. Fortunately, as will be seen in the next section, this is not the case.

The Transmission Cost Function

In the previous section, an average cost function was derived with the following functional form (see note 3):

$$c_{ij} = a + b^*/x_{ij}. \tag{4.3}$$

This function was fitted to average cost data found in *The 1970 National Power Survey*.[4] The following equation fitted this data best (the standard errors of the estimates are in parentheses):

$$c_{ij} = \underset{(0.07637)}{0.81904} + \underset{(0.02863)}{0.20183}/x_{ij} \tag{4.4}$$

$R^2 = 0.96132$

where c_{ij} = mills per kWh per 200 miles, and

x_{ij} = flow from i to j in thousand megawatts.

From equation (4.4) the fixed and marginal costs of transmission in mills per kWh per mile are 0.0040952 and 0.00100915, respectively. The value of a in the problem is then 0.0040952. To test the sensitivity of the important results to these estimates of transmission costs, both higher and lower costs can also be used.

Note in passing that the time (intertemporal) element is not considered explicitly. It is simply assumed, as does the Federal Power Commission, that the marginal transmission cost is time-invariant.[5]

Interregional Transmission Cost

Nine demand points are used in the model for the purpose of measuring the distance between region *i* and region *j* (d_{ij}). The demand areas are gross. It is obviously difficult to pick a single point as representative of each of the regions. Weighing each set of coordinates in each region by the consumption of electrical energy at that point would yield an average consuming point. The average distance travelled by each kWh of electrical energy through each region would represent another possible point. A third possibility would be to choose points which maximize the distance that electrical energy has to travel. The method actually used is a combination of all three, with the first and second most heavily relied upon. It is assumed that the d_{ij}'s, as for the c_{ij}'s, are time invariant. Notationally, the cost of transmission from region *i* to region *j* is $c^*_{ij} = d_{ij}\, c_{ij}$. The actual distances between regions that are used can be found in Table 4-1.

Distribution Cost

Electric power distribution facilities are designed to subdivide bulk power and deliver it at suitable voltages to the individual users. They include step-down transformers, which reduce transmission voltages, low voltage primary and secondary distribution lines or feeders, consumer service transformers, and connecting services to consumer's premises. Growth in the number of electric consumers and in average use per consumer are the principal factors affecting the requirements for new facilities and additional investments necessary to meet future service needs.[6]

Throughout the history of the electrical energy industry, there has been a steady downward trend in the average cost of electrical energy per kWh sold to consumers. Since nearly 40 percent of the investment in electric utilities is in distributional facilities, the trend of distribution system cost will be a major factor in determining the cost of electrical energy over the next twenty years.

The cost data and forecasts are obtained directly from *The 1970 National Power Survey* and represent totals and averages for all electric utilities in the contiguous United States. No attempt has been made to break them down by region, type of ownership, or any other system of classification. Unit costs of individual utilities have in the past and will in the future vary considerably from the national average because of differences in climate, topography, load density, lead characteristics, growth rates, type of ownership, size of utility, and so on. However, given the low level of resolution (i.e., the regional breakdown), the regional averages will closely approximate the national value and hence this value will be used across all regions.[7]

Table 4-1
Distance between Regions
(Miles)

	NE	*MA*	*ENC*	*WNC*	*SA*	*ESC*	*WSC*	*M*	*P*
1. New England	0	216	994	1454	1074	1190	1821	1997	3162
2. Middle Atlantic		0	840	1209	862	978	1605	1866	3031
3. East North Central			0	504	730	653	937	1013	2187
4. West North Central				0	805	713	937	606	1871
5. South Atlantic					0	154	820	1411	2543
6. East South Central						0	665	1302	2391
7. West South Central							0	784	1763
8. Mountain								0	1264
9. Pacific									0

The cost of distribution consists of investment cost and the annual cost of distribution. Investment cost encompasses costs for distribution substations, overhead lines, underground lines, meters, installations on consumer's property, and street light and signal systems. The overhead and underground lines together represent more than 70 percent of this total. The annual cost of distribution consists of fixed charges on investment and operation and maintenance expenses. Fixed charges include return on invested capital, depreciation, taxes, and insurance.

During the 15 year period 1952-1967, the average kWh use, distribution system investment, and distribution operation and maintenance expenses per final consumer were increasing annually. However, because kWh use was increasing more rapidly than either investment or operation and maintenance expenses, the trends of distribution investment and expense per kWh were downward.

These trends serve as the basis for projecting future cost per kWh to 1990. Specifically, the figures for future investment and operation and maintenance expenses for 1980 and 1990 are obtained by extrapolating the historical trends of these costs. The intermediate figures (e.g., 1975) are obtained from a simple interpolation of the values.

The projected values are the levels that would be experienced if these costs continued to follow the historical trends until 1990. Long range forecasting of costs is subject to numerous uncertainties, and it is improbable that these costs will closely follow the extrapolated trend curve through this period. The past trend of distribution costs has been influenced by several factors, some of which tend to increase cost per kWh and others which tend to decrease it.

The two principal factors that have made possible the decreasing trend in distribution cost are increasing load density and technological progress. Other cost reducing factors include better communications, which improve utilization of maintenance crews and equipment, greater mechanization of maintenance operations, expanded use of supervisory control and automation, and increased use of computers. It is expected that these factors will continue to influence distribution cost downward in the future, but probably with some decrease in effectiveness.[8]

The principal factors that influence the trend of distribution cost in the upward direction are rising prices of materials and labor, increasing standards of service reliability, increasing cost and difficulty of acquiring properly located substation sites, increasing costs of meeting location appearance criteria for both lines and substations and added costs of constructing a greater proportion of facilities underground.[9]

Because of the uncertainties involved in long range forecasting of future cost, the Federal Power Commission estimates the probable ranges within which the future costs will fall subject to three assumptions: (1) the average fixed charges will remain at approximately the same level, (2) prices of distribution materials and labor will continue to increase at an average annual rate of about 2.4 percent, and (3) there will be no substantial increase in the historical rate of expenditures for converting overhead lines to underground.[10] The middle value of each of the ranges will be used in the computations here.

The probable value of the distribution cost per kWh sold to all final consumers then, given the above considerations, is 5.18 mills for 1970, 5.10 mills for 1975, 5.025 mills for 1980, 4.9725 mills for 1985, and 4.92 mills for 1990.[11] These figures are in constant 1970 dollars.

Note that when interregional transmission of electrical energy was considered in the first part of this chapter, one faced the possibility of a zero fixed cost when there was no flow between regions; however, for distribution there is assumed always to be a positive intraregional flow. This means that the fixed cost component of distribution is always incurred.

The Cost Functions

A fundamental feature of electrical energy supply is that, as an enterprise, it provides consumers with two services: (1) the actual energy consumed and (2) a readiness to supply the energy the consumer wants whenever he wants it. Thus, it comes about that the total cost incurred by a utility in supplying electrical energy falls into two categories: (1) the variable cost component and (2) the fixed cost component.

Formally, one looks at the problem of the estimation of the cost function with a view to incorporating the peculiarities of the industry. The existence of increasing returns to scale in electrical energy generation and the problems of operating existing facilities and of investing in new generating capacity are important characteristics. It is fairly well established now that increasing returns to scale do exist in the generation of electrical energy.[12] Given this is the case (and hence a steadily falling marginal cost curve), it would be incorrect to view supply as consisting of the traditional upward sloping schedule.[13] Secondly, the decision to build new generating capacity is based on peak power requirements of a specific utility. Overcapacity penalizes the utility with higher than necessary average cost. An undercapacity results in a deficiency in reliability and quality of service to final consumers.

Now consider the two categories of total cost with a view towards empirically estimating the cost function. The first is the variable cost consisting of fuel cost, labor cost, plant operating supplies, maintenance renewal parts, and so on. Variable cost per kWh does not vary with the level of output of a generating plant. This category as it is typically viewed is horizontal up to the point of maximum existing generating capacity at which point it becomes vertical (perfectly inelastic). (The variable cost of operation for any existing plant might conceivably slope upward slightly due to increased fuel cost associated with a larger output; but, this does not appear to be the case.)[14] The second cost component is the capital cost associated with addition to existing capacity. This, together with variable cost, makes up the long-run marginal cost of production.

The variable cost is much less than long-run marginal cost. Estimates by the Federal Power Commission, for example, of the long-run marginal cost of producing electrical energy by steam generation is approximately 0.73 cents per kWh of which 0.08 cents is for labor, 0.31 cents is for fuel, and 0.34 cents is for capital cost.[15] Summarily, long-run marginal cost (specifically capital cost) and variable cost are separate considerations of the problem.

A Problem of Cost Minimization

If one abstracts for the moment from the consideration of net social payoff maximization to facilitate exposition by taking demand considerations to be exogenous, the overall problem can be looked at from a cost minimization point of view. There is a good general survey of the approaches to this problem that need not be repeated here.[16] What is needed, however, is to adapt the general considerations to the specific case of electrical energy generation.

The problem of determining optimum investment policies (i.e., capital cost considerations) given rapid increase in demand and a number and diversity of alternative investment policies has motivated the development of several mathematical models to assist in evaluating alternatives. Investment decision variables of the industry interact strongly at a point in time and over time. This happens for two reasons. First, different energy sources have complementary functions in the interconnected power systems. The main sources of electrical energy are hydroelectric schemes, fossil-fueled steam-electric plants (coal, oil and gas), and nuclear-steam (thermal) reactors. Nuclear plants have high capital cost but low generation (operation, maintenance, and fuel) cost, while fossil-fueled plants have high capital cost and slightly higher generation cost. Hydroelectric plants have high or low capital cost (depending on the site) and near zero generation cost, but are hampered by constraints on output stemming from their multipurpose nature and from water inflow variation. The optimum balance of plants in the system at any point in time will depend on the relative capital and generation costs of the alternative energy sources.

Second, the optimum balance will depend on the existing and expected structure of the system. For example, more nuclear and less fossil fuel in future years means that the future system fuel savings of hydroelectric schemes installed now will be less. A large nuclear power program in future years may thus shift the present balance towards more fossil-fueled and more hydroelectric plants. Similarly, if the existing structure is predominantly fossil-fueled, then the present emphasis will be more nuclear and/or hydroelectric plants to save on system fuel cost.[17]

Because of these interactions among decision variables, the model has to be multidimensional and cast in terms of historical dynamics. The investment decisions to be made in the current period depend on the past and future development of investments and hence upon the past and future structure of factor prices.

Before the model is specified, limitations of the approach should be made clear. First, use of an investment model is really only the first of several stages of the investment decision process. Engineering analysis of solutions follows and generally requires a revision of the solutions. The investment program has to satisfy certain engineering and economic requirements and this is an iterative, multidimensional process. Second, all of the formulations presented are deterministic. Allowances can be made for uncertainties in demand, plant availability, and flows of water to hydroelectric schemes, but this takes the form of margins of spare capacity. Third, there is no discussion of terminal conditions as analyzed by Hopkins[18] or Littlechild.[19] This, of course, does not preclude the inclusion of terminal conditions in a variant of the model.

In attempting to formalize the problem, one notices that electrical energy, given the above considerations, is an example of a joint product.[20] An input of equipment provides capacity in a technically fixed proportion during each period. However, it is not necessary that production in each period equal capacity. Additionally, generating equipment provides capacity over its lifetime in fixed proportions, but it will not necessarily be optimal to maintain production at full capacity.

Since electrical energy is not produced in fixed proportions over a period, one cannot "define a compound unit of output...and treat it as a single output."[21] Neither can one apply the analysis for varying proportions because the cost and production functions lose differentiability at certain points.[22]

The initial formulation of the problem was presented in 1968 by Turvey,[23] and since then some refinements have been made. The formulation used here (still considering for the moment a cost-minimizing approach) is detailed in what follows. Formally, choose nonnegative levels of production, x_{jt}^{Θ}, in periods $t = 1, 2, \ldots, T$, in regions $j = 1, 2, \ldots, N$ and with plant type $\Theta = 1, 2, \ldots, L$, where $\Theta = 1$, the hydroelectric scheme, $\Theta = 2$, fossil-fueled plants (coal, oil, and gas) and $\Theta = 3$, nuclear plants, in the current period; and a nonnegative amount of each type of plant input, W^{Θ}_{jt}, that will be supplied in the current period, t, to meet demand. The value of this term will be in kWh of new capacity. This is more fully discussed in the subsequent chapter.

The operating rule as given by Turvey[24] (with the exception of the inclusion of a discount factor, which is considered in chapter 6) is to minimize

$$\sum_t \left[\sum_j \sum_\Theta \Psi^{\Theta}_{jt} x^{\Theta}_{jt} + \sum_j \sum_\Theta \xi^{\Theta}_{jt} W^{\Theta}_{jt} \right] \tag{4.5}$$

with Ψ^{Θ}_{jt} being the marginal cost of operation of plant type Θ and ξ^{Θ}_{jt} being the marginal cost of additional capacity of plant type Θ that is being added in period t. Note that no consideration is explicitly given to terminal capacity bequeathed to period $T + 1$.

There are constraints that must be imposed on the current levels of production as well as on the additions to capacity. All of the constraints will be discussed in chapter 6, but it is relevant to consider a few of the restrictions at this point.[25] For the moment, as one thinks forward to the empirical implementation of the model, one should look at the following constraints: (1) For each type of plant, Θ, in a given period, t, and a given region, j, actual production cannot exceed capacity:

$$x^{\Theta}_{jt} \leq \frac{1}{(1+r^{\Theta})^{t-1}} S^{\Theta}_{j1} + \sum_{\tau=1}^{t} \frac{1}{(1+r^{\Theta})^{t-\tau}} W^{\Theta}_{jt} \tag{4.6}$$

where x^{Θ}_{jt} = the level of generation in region j from plant type Θ,

S^{Θ}_{j1} = the actual capacity existing in region j at the beginning of period 1 for plant type Θ,

W^{Θ}_{jt} = the addition to capacity in period t for region j for plant type Θ,

r^{Θ} = the rate of depreciation on a generating plant of type Θ.

(2) Total output, $\Sigma_j x_{jit}$, is less than or equal to the sum of production on generating equipment of all types for any given region, j, and time period, t:

$$\sum_j x_{jit} \leq \sum_\Theta x^{\Theta}_{jt} \tag{4.7}$$

(3) For each plant type (hydroelectric, fossil-fueled, and nuclear) investment is constrained by physical, institutional, and technological limitations:

$$W^{\Theta}_{jt} \leq \tilde{W}^{\Theta}_{jt} \tag{4.8}$$

where $\tilde{W}^{\Theta}_{jt}$ is the constraint on investment.

The Variable Cost—Fossil-Fueled Steam-Electric Plants

The cost functions of economic theory that are employed here are timeless abstractions, while the data available to estimate these functions are observations from different time periods. Hence, this requires an assumption that the relationship has changed in a definable and measurable way. There are a large number of factors making for shifts in the cost function (obsolescence of plant, changed management techniques, different production methods, and so on), all of which are not likely to show startling changes in the same year. One might assume that the combined overall effect of these factors moves slowly and smoothly with time. However, reflecting on the discussions of the estimation of the demand relations from chapter 2, it is not appropriate to have time as a major explanatory variable in the cost equations if data are available on the factors making for shifts. This is the approach taken here.

Consider the average variable cost (which annually is equal to the marginal cost because of the assumed horizontal nature of the cost function) of conventional fossil-fueled (coal, oil, and gas) steam-electric plants. Because of data limitations, one is required to rely on a weighted average annual production expense. It is weighted by fuel type, and it is assumed for projection purposes, that the changing proportion of generation of electrical energy by fuel type will maintain the past trend. Based on industry projections, this is not an unrealistic assumption.[26] Another assumption that is required because of data limitations is that the average cost is equal across all regions. (This is assumed for other types of generating plants also.) This is slightly unrealistic because the proportion of fuel types used in conventional fossil plants in, say, the New England region, which relies on a mixture of coal, oil, and gas is not the same as that of the plants in the West South Central region, where gas has a basic monopoly as fuel.[27] There is a spatial difference in the price of fuels that would be reflected in a regional differentiation in average cost. However, given the available alternatives, the assumption of a uniform cost across regions is the best.

The principal component of variable cost is fuel cost, which accounted for 80 percent of total production expense in 1970. The major component of the remaining cost is that of labor. Plant operating supplies, miscellaneous materials, and maintenance renewal parts make up the balance of the 20 percent. Power plants vary widely in size, operating steam conditions, delivered fuel cost, heat rates and annual plant factors, all of which affect total production expense per net kWh. All of these factors are taken into account when the average annual variable cost of producing electrical energy per kWh is computed.[28]

There have been several studies that have been concerned with estimating cost functions for the fossil-fueled steam-electric plant. They are surveyed in Galatin's volume, and that survey need not be repeated here.[29] All published studies have taken the plant or firm as the unit of observation and never has the industry as a whole been investigated. The majority of the studies have found increasing returns to scale in the generation of electrical energy.

It is felt that since the industry as a whole is the focus of the analysis, it is the economically relevant entity. The industry, not single plants, are regulated and it is at the industry level that investment decisions should be made.[30]

Given that variable cost is a function of the level of output, wage rates, fuel cost, and technology, the functional specification should take account of these factors.[31] However, in preliminary analyses, it was found that neither wage rates nor the price of fuels were statistically significant explanatory variables. This result is not surprising in light of the empirical studies cited by Galatin.[32] Consequently, it is assumed that cost is simply a function of output and technological change.

The measurement of the technological change factor is extremely difficult. Operating steam conditions, heat rates, and annual plant factors all affect total production expenses as do slowdowns, speedups, and improvements in the education of the labor force. All sorts of things will appear as technological change.[33] In an effort to explain a realistic portion of this change, national average heat rates for fossil-fueled steam-electric plants are used.[34] Given that fuel cost accounts for roughly 80 percent of production expense, any increase in thermal efficiency should have a measurable impact on decreasing cost and should account for a good portion of the effects of technological change. Additionally, thermal efficiency will reflect the changing composition in age and type of plants. That is, as new plants are brought into the generation process and as there is a shift away from coal to gas and oil plants, the production expense will fall.[35]

Several alternative functional specifications were tried. The one that fit the data best was the form:

$$AC_{2t} = B_{21} X_{2out\,t}^{q21} e^{sTE_t + \epsilon_{21t}} \tag{4.9}$$

where AC_2 = the average annual production expense,

X_{2out}^{q21} = the net generation,

TE = thermal efficiency,

t = tth year, and

B_{21}, q_{21} and s are unknown parameters and ϵ_{21} is the error term.

This specification is a simple generalization of a constant elasticity cost function and has considerable intuitive appeal. It argues that variable cost is not solely a function of the level of output along a constant elasticity curve.[36] There is an exponential drift that incorporates the effects of, among other things, technological change and the age and type of plant.

Given that the objective in estimating the cost function is to project via regression techniques the future variable cost of the production of electrical energy for the periods up to 1990, it is necessary to determine a relationship between thermal efficiency and variables exogenous to the model. Effectively, this comes down to projecting technological change for fossil-fueled steam-electric plants. Technological progress is intimately dependent on economic phenomena.[37] There are many factors that make for technological change, which in turn make for shifts in the cost function. All the factors are not likely to change radically in the same year, so the assumption of a combined overall slow and smooth change with time is realistic. Thus, time is used as a proxy for all the factors contributing to technological progress.[38]

The functional form that best explains the level of thermal efficiency is of the following form:

$$e^{TE_t} = B_{22} T_t^{q_{22}} e^{\epsilon_{22t}} \qquad (4.10)$$

where TE = thermal efficiency,

T = the year (i.e., 1947, 1948, etc.),

t = tth year, and

B_{22} and q_{22} are unknown parameters and ϵ_{22} is the error term.

In obtaining the empirical results for the model, annual observations on each variable in the model were obtained for the United States from 1947 to 1970. The exact specifications of the variables found to be significant and used to explain the average cost relationship are found in Table 4-2.

The average cost variable is measured in constant 1970 dollars deflated by the wholesale price index. First, the deflation of that data was undertaken because the theory of cost curves traces out the implications of various hypotheses about the production function on the assumption that factor prices are constant and independent of the purchases of a firm.[39] Actual cost observations come from a time period during which prices have changed substantially in response to influences other than the firm's purchases. Secondly, the wholesale price index was chosen as the factor price deflator because the inputs into the electrical energy generation process are so varied that even if price indices for each input existed, the computational burden of factor-specific deflation would be prohibitive.

Now if one linearizes equations (4.9) and (4.10) using a simple logarithmic (log to the base e) transformation, the following equations result:

$$\log AC_{2t} = \log B_{21} + q_{21} \log X_{2out_t} + sTE_t + \epsilon_{21t} \quad (4.11)$$

$$TE_t = \log B_{22} + q_{22} \log T_t + \epsilon_{22t} \quad (4.12)$$

When both equations are inspected together, it becomes apparent that they constitute a simultaneous system. Further, if it is assumed that $E(\epsilon_{21t}, \epsilon_{22t}) = 0$, then these equations are a diagonally recursive system of simultaneous equations and the estimation problem becomes really simple. The reason is that the endogenous variables are not correlated with the error term of the equation in which they appear.[40] This means that application of the ordinary least squares method to each of the structural equations (i.e., (4.11) and (4.12)) leads to consistent and asymptotically efficient estimates.[41]

The estimates for equations (4.11) and (4.12), respectively, are (with the standard errors of the estimates in parentheses):

$$\log AC_{2t} = \underset{(0.09695)}{3.3488} - \underset{(0.04026)}{0.13549} \log X_{2out_t} - \underset{(0.005969)}{0.031833}\, TE_t \quad (4.13)$$

$R^2 = 0.9726$ d.w. $= 1.245$

$$TE_t = -\underset{(636.74)}{7493.5} + \underset{(84.003)}{992.46} \log T_t \quad (4.14)$$

$R^2 = 0.8638$ d.w. $= 0.1184$

These results are not surprising, being fully consistent with a priori expectations. There is evidence of a marked degree of increasing returns to scale at the industry level. Additionally, as thermal efficiency increases, the average cost curve falls. Even with the potential aggregation problems lurking behind the scene,[42] the values obtained are consistent with other, though more disaggregated, studies of fossil-fueled steam-electric generation. The Durbin-Watson statistic falls in the inconclusive region for equation (4.13). The relation between thermal efficiency and time comes out as expected. There is a strong positive trend toward increased thermal efficiency over time. As one would expect, the Durbin-Watson statistic indicates a positive serial correlation. This is because the residuals contain values that are correlated over time, but, due to the qualitative nature of the factors affecting thermal efficiency, little can be done to rectify the deficiency.

The Variable Cost-Nuclear Steam-Electric Plants

Whereas there has been a superabundance of work on estimating cost

Table 4-2
Specification of Variables and Their Source Used in Estimation

Variable	*Units of Measurement*
AC—Average Annual Production Expense[a]	Mills per kilowatt-hour (deflated)
X_{out} —Net Generation[b]	Billions of kilowatt-hours
TE—Thermal Efficiency—National Average Heat Rate for Fossil-Fueled Steam-Electric Plants (Total Electric Power Industry)[c]	Percent
T—Time	Actual year (e.g., 1947)

[a]Source: Federal Power Commission, *Statistics of Privately Owned Electric Utilities in the United States,* U.S. Government Printing Office, Washington, various years. These data are for classes A and B companies (i.e., companies with annual operating revenues of one million dollars or more).

[b]Source: Same as footnote a.

[c]Source: Federal Power Commission *Steam-Electric Plant Construction Cost and Annual Production Expenses,* U.S. Government Printing Office, Washington, 1973.

functions for conventional fossil-fueled steam-electric plants, there has been no work on estimating cost functions for nuclear steam-electric plants. This is because at the end of 1971 there were only 20 nuclear units in commercial operation (versus 555 conventional fossil-fueled plants) with the first plant being put into commercial operation in 1961.[43] Sufficient time has elapsed however to provide enough observations to enable one to estimate a variable cost function for nuclear steam-electric plants. One must be cautious however when projecting future cost with such a short time series. It remains to be seen whether the projections are consistent with other expectations.

There are several types of nuclear generating plants (light water reactor, boiling water reactor, high temperature gas cooled reactor, and so on) but as with the fossil-fueled steam-electric plants, a weighted average annual production expense will be relied upon.

Principal annual production cost components are maintenance and operation costs. Fuel cost accounted for 62 percent of total production expense in 1970. Nuclear fuel cost is influenced by many more factors than is fossil fuel cost. There are many steps in the overall cycle cost.

The main cost component of the remaining 38 percent is labor. On graphing operation and maintenance cost for various size nuclear generating units, one again sees the increasing returns to scale that were observed empirically for conventional steam plants.[44] The reason for the decrease in cost is that few additional personnel are required as the size of the nuclear units increase and as a second unit is added at a site, the operating portion of the cost does not increase proportionately. One component of operation and maintenance costs for nuclear plants that the conventional steam plants and the hydroelectric plants do not possess is nuclear insurance, which amounts to about 30 percent of the operation and maintenance cost, which is expected to remain fairly constant.[45] All of the operation and maintenance costs components are taken into account when computing the average annual cost of generating electrical energy per kWh by nuclear plants.

The industry as a whole is the focus of the analysis and hence it is the economically relevant entity. Average variable cost is a function of the level of output, fuel cost, wage rates and technological change. Preliminary analysis did not find wage rates or fuel cost statistically significant explanatory variables. Additionally, whereas in the case of conventional fossil-fueled steam-electric plants there was a ready measure of technological change, no such indicator is available for nuclear plants. Consequently, a time was used as a proxy for technological change but all functional specifications yielded insignificant results. This probably resulted because of either a problem of multicollinearity between time and output[46] or the paucity of data so that a definite shift in the average variable cost due to technological change could not be separated from the economies of scale phenomenon.

Of the several functional specifications tried, the one fitting the data best was the constant elasticity form

$$AC_{3t} = B_3 X_{3out_t}^{\alpha 3} e^{\epsilon_{3t}} \tag{4.15}$$

where the variable definitions correspond to those following equation (4.9). The specification argues that variable cost is solely a function of the level of output along a constant elasticity curve.

In obtaining the empirical estimates of the model parameters, annual observations on each variable were obtained for the United States from 1963 to 1970.[47] The specification of the variables is found in Table 4-2. The average variable cost is in constant 1970 dollars.

The parameter estimates via ordinary least squares for equation (4.15), after a simple logarithmic transformation is performed (with the standard errors of the estimates in parentheses), is

$$\log AC_{3t} = \underset{(0.05239)}{2.465} - \underset{(0.02716)}{0.43097} \log X_{3out_t} \tag{4.16}$$

$R^2 = 0.97671 \quad d.w. = 3.0565$

The results are consistent with a priori expectations. There is evidence of increasing returns to scale. The Durbin-Watson statistic is inconclusive.

Note in passing that when the average variable cost of production for nuclear plants is considered, it is assumed that annually average cost is equal to the marginal cost of production because of the assumed horizontal nature of the cost function.

The Variable Cost—Hydroelectric Plants

There has been no work on estimating cost functions for various hydroelectric schemes. Because of data limitations (the data cannot be separated), both the cost of conventional hydroelectric schemes and pumped hydroelectric schemes are aggregated together in the consideration of the variable cost function.[48] This seems fully justified because operating costs appear to be the same for the two different types.[49]

No fuel cost is incurred when hydroelectric energy is generated. This proves to reduce significantly operation and maintenance expenses and gives hydroelectric plants a distinct advantage over other types of plants. Unfortunately, most readily available sites for economical production of hydroelectric energy have been developed, so there is a limit to which one can take advantage of this cost differential.[50]

The average variable cost (which annually is equal to the marginal cost because of the assumed horizontal cost function) is dependent upon the level of output, wage rates and technology. Annual hydroelectric system production expense per net kWh varies across systems. Size, age, load factor, and joint cost allocation all contribute to this variance. Ideally, regional production expenses would be available, but practically they are not. Consequently, national aggregate values are used to estimate the average cost function for hydroelectric generation.

There have not been the technological innovations in hydroelectric generation comparable to say, the increased thermal efficiency found in conventional fossil-fueled steam-electric generation. The significant trends are toward larger units and lower plant capacity factors, which are reflected in the increasing returns to scale. As a matter of fact, upon using a time variable as proxy for technological change, under several different functional specifications, technological change did not prove to be significant in explaining the level of the average annual production expense. Kendrick's factor productivity variable[51] was also used as a measure for technological change (over the shorter period 1948-1966), still to no avail.

Additionally, other preliminary tests did not find wage rates to be a statistically significant explanatory variable.

Once again the best functional specification is the constant elasticity model. Specifically,

$$AC_{1t} = B_1 \, X_{1out_t}^{q_1} \, e^{\epsilon_{1t}} \qquad (4.17)$$

where the variable definitions are the same as those following equation (4.9).

To estimate the unknown parameters (B_1 and q_1), time series observations on average annual production expense and net generation for hydroelectric plants over the period 1947 to 1970 are used. The units of the variables can be found in Table 4-2. Average annual production expense is in constant 1970 dollars.

The parameters were estimated by ordinary least squares. To accomplish this, equation (4.17) was linearized with a logarithmic transformation. The results (with the standard errors of the estimates in parentheses) are:

$$\log AC_{1t} = \underset{(0.27646)}{2.3401} - \underset{(0.06814)}{0.54607} \log X_{1out_t} \qquad (4.18)$$

$R^2 = 0.7448$ d.w. = 1.199

Not surprisingly, there is evidence of increasing returns to scale. What is surprising though is the relatively low multiple correlation coefficient (i.e., R is low relative to the other plant types.) The indication is that another variable or variables explain more than twenty-five percent of the variation in annual production expense. These other factors are not immediately apparent. The Durbin-Watson statistic proves inconclusive for testing serial correlation.

Capital Costs—Conventional Fossil-Fueled Steam-Electric Plants and Nuclear Steam-Electric Plants

As peak power requirements expand, the electrical energy industry expands existing generating capacity to meet the demand. The capital cost, i.e., the cost of adding new plant and equipment, greatly influences the total cost for any type of power generation. For example, average annual production expense was about 3.47 mills/kWh for nuclear units in 1970, with total cost of electrical energy generation from nuclear plants ordered in 1970 in the neighborhood of 10-12 mills/kWh.

The selection of a plant that will provide the most economic generation of electrical energy while complying with environmental requirements will be influenced by many factors. Thus accurate estimates of capital costs are essential in comparing the economic merits of different types of power plants.

Plant investment is summarized in terms of land, structures, and equipment. In many instances the cost for a new single unit plant includes embedded expenditures for future unit extensions. Land, general site improvements, circulating water, and fuel storage and handling facilities are among the types of expenditures that would properly be reallocated when new units are added.

Plant location, number of units, unit size, kind of fuel burned, steam pressures and temperatures, cooling water requirements, control of stack emissions, indoor or outdoor construction, foundation conditions, provisions for future units, construction labor costs and labor available all have a bearing on unit investment cost.

Three computer programs, which are referred to as the CONCEPT package, have been developed at Oak Ridge National Laboratory and the Computer Technology Center[52] and are designed to provide a means of estimating future capital cost of different plants under various sets of economic and technical specifications incorporating the foregoing considerations. The procedures used in CONCEPT are based on the assumption that any central station power plant of the same type involves approximately the same major cost components, regardless of location or date of initial operation. Therefore, if trends of these major cost components can be established as a function of time, location and plant type and size, a cost estimate can be obtained for any case of interest.

The cost model for nuclear and conventional fossil-fueled steam-electric plants is based on a detailed cost estimate for a reference plant at a designated time and location. Each estimate includes a detailed breakdown of each cost account into costs for equipment, labor and materials. These components are segregated, an appropriate cost index applied that accounts for variation among regions and over time, and then they are summed to account for an adjusted total cost. Three sets of cost indexes are used to adjust the cost of equipment, labor, and materials. The equipment cost indexes are calculated from functional relations, and the labor cost indexes are calculated from basic parameters, which include wage rates for the various crafts, labor productivity, and overtime considerations. The materials cost indexes are calculated from unit costs for site-related materials, which include structural steel, reinforcing steel, concrete, and lumber.

The following assumptions are made in the program: (1) Costs are referenced to start of design and construction, (2) 40-hour workweek with no overtime, and (3) constant 7 percent per year simple interest for calculating interest during construction.

The cost model was developed from investment cost studies and detailed cost estimates for hypothetical 1000-megawatt plants which were prepared for the U.S. Atomic Energy Commission.[53] The hypothetical plants are assumed to be located at the AEC Middletown site. This site is favorable in all respects, including an adequate supply of cooling water, low population density, satisfactory transportation facilities, and sufficient labor supply for a 40-hour workweek.[54]

Direct costs, being a function of plant size, are described by equations fitted to cost-size scaling curves. These curves are estimated to be representative of capital cost for unit sizes in the range 500 megawatts to about 1500 megawatts.

The cost model for each type of plant includes distribution of labor and materials. These are used in calculating cost indexes for adjusting base costs to other locations and for projecting costs into the future.

The calculation of interest during construction requires a cash flow curve for each cost category. These cash flow curves are assumed to be approximately the same for similar types of plants. The curves are normalized, so the range of both axes is from zero to one. The origin corresponds to the date of placing the order for the power plant. Approximately 0.3 on the abscissa corresponds to the date of issuance of the construction permit and the start of actual construction and 1.0 corresponds to date of commercial operation.

Indirect costs (engineering and construction management services, construction facilities equipment and services, and other costs) are assumed to be functions of total physical plant direct cost, including allowances for spare parts and contingencies.

The labor cost data consist of hourly rates (including fringe benefits) for 16 classifications of craft labor.[55] The materials cost data consist of market quotations for seven classifications of materials.[56] The data cover the period 1960 through 1972 on a semiannual basis. The productivity of craft labor is difficult to define and, practically, varies significantly not only country-wide but within a single locale depending on such factors as the availability of equipment and weather. Consequently, no effort was made to include productivity factors for the normal workweek.

The foregoing is a general description of the methodology employed in computing the capital cost estimates for steam-electric power plants. A more complete explication and mathematical formulation of the relationships can be found in the user's manual for CONCEPT[57] and is reproduced in the Appendix without change of notation.

Capital Cost—Hydroelectric Plants

Unfortunately a program similar to CONCEPT does not exist for estimating hydroelectric power plant capital cost. However, just as in the situation for thermal electric plants, year-to-year and plant-to-plant differences in investment cost per kilowatt reflect primarily the wide variations in type, size and location of projects, cost of land and relocation of existing roads and structures, and to a lesser extent changes in labor, materials, engineering and other factors in construction costs. Investment cost per kilowatt continues (and is expected to continue) to be substantially higher for conventional hydroelectric plants than for the thermal-electric plants.[58]

Cost data adequate for making economic analyses of most potential hydroelectric sites are not available.[59] Therefore, any projection of new units to be constructed during the period to 1990 is highly conjectural. Further, it was formerly the case that engineering and economic feasibility were dominant factors in considering the development of a hydroelectric project. In recent years, however, environmental factors have assumed ever-increasing importance and the ecological and social consequences of a proposed project may now determine its fate.[60]

The relative scarcity in many parts of the country of conventional hydroelectric sites capable of providing large amounts of capacity to meet peak period demand, and the economies made possible by the development of reversible equipment that can be used for both pumping and generating, have resulted in a sharp increase in the planning and construction of pumped storage projects. During the next 20 years, the installation of pumped storage capacity is expected to exceed greatly the installation of new conventional capacity. As reported in the *1970 National Power Survey*, conventional hydroelectric capacity is projected to total approximately 82 million kilowatts by 1990. Pumped storage capacity is projected to climb to about 70 million kilowatts. For 1972, the comparable values are 53 million and 4 million kilowatts, respectively.[61] Additionally, whereas the operation and maintenance cost of the conventional and pumped hydroelectric projects are approximately the same, capital costs differ, being about 2.33 times as great for the conventional hydroelectric plant.[62]

The above considerations, then, force the use of a value for combined capital cost for conventional and pumped hydroelectric projects that is not calculated directly as for fossil-fueled steam-electric plants and nuclear steam plants. If one looks at the capital cost estimates provided by the Federal Power Commission in 1970, a ratio of from 1.1 to 1.3 across regions of the capital cost of a combination of conventional hydroelectric plants and pumped hydroelectric plants to comparable size fossil-fueled steam-electric plants is observed.[63] This regularity allows the use of the CONCEPT program with the appropriate multiplicative constant in computing capital cost for the hydroelectric system.[64] This is the procedure that shall be followed. Implicit in this procedure is the assumption that this ratio will remain constant throughout the period.

5 Cost Projections for Electrical Energy

The methodology used in obtaining short-run cost estimates for fossil-fueled steam-electric and hydroelectric plants is the same as that discussed in chapter 3. Nuclear steam plants present some special problems. Capital cost estimates are evolved from the CONCEPT program. Additionally, empirical estimates of the supply constraints detailed under "Distribution Costs" in chapter 4 are discussed.

Projecting Variable Costs to 1990

Variable cost projections for fossil-fueled steam-electric and hydroelectric plants are obtained by using coefficients of the average variable cost curves determined in chapter 4, the likely change in net generation, and for conventional fossil plants, the likely change in thermal efficiency. The expected change is obtained from industry projections, while the likely change in thermal efficiency is dependent only on the time factor and does not rely on the predicted level of any exogenous variable.

The forecast methodology employed is discussed under "Projection" in chapter 3. Time trend analysis, multiple regression techniques, and judgment are all employed. The level of the independent variables are predicted beforehand, and it is assumed there is no measurement error.

The estimation of net generation is obtained from the *24th Annual Electrical Industry Forecast*.[1] What is presented in this forecast for each plant type is net additions to generating capacity. Net additions are related to net generation by a capacity factor (alternately called a capacity of utilization factor), which is just net generation divided by the number of hours in a given year times installed capacity. This factor has remained constant for the various plant types over the past 15 years[2] and is expected to remain unchanged for at least the next 20 years.[3] Given the factor constancy, one can compute from net additions to capacity, the net generation that is expected to obtain over the years 1971 to 1990. The projections of net additions to capacity are based on the assumptions that power station construction will be allowed to be completed on schedule, that there will be no additional governmental restrictions or rationing of electrical energy, and that industry executives will retain the right to make prudent management decisions in the planning, construction, and operation of power systems.[4]

For hydroelectric plants, few available sites remain undeveloped. However, in recent years increasing amounts of conventional hydroelectric capacity have been reassigned from base-load to peaking operations and this has spurred the addition of generating units to existing stations. Pumped hydroelectric facilities, not being as site-limited as conventional hydroelectric plants, also are able to accept or reject large blocks of load very quickly, making them more flexible than steam-electric plants. They are being added specifically for peak load operation.[5] It is projected that between 1970 and 1990 net additions to capacity and net generation will increase by 96.912 percent. Broken down incrementally (with 1970 as the base period), the period 1971 to 1975 will find a 4.65 annual percentage increase, the period 1976 to 1980 will find a 11.1 annual percentage increase, and the period 1981 to 1990 will find a 1.18 annual percentage increase. The large annual increase in the period 1976-1980 is accounted for mainly by the pumped hydroelectric additions.

Fossil-fueled steam-electric plant generation is expected to expand, though not at quite the same rate as projected for hydroelectric plant generation. Fossil-fueled steam-electric plants have long been the mainstay of the electrical energy industry, accounting for 81 percent of installed generating capacity in 1970. With increased reliance on nuclear power, conventional fossil plants will be added only to the extent necessary to meet the demand that nuclear plants and hydroelectric plants are unable to satisfy. This means that fossil-fueled steam-electric plant generation is expected to increase 7.35 percent annually between 1971 and 1975, 6.25 percent annually between 1976 and 1980, 1.26 annually between 1981 and 1985, and 1.27 percent annually between 1986 and 1990, using 1970 as the base period. It is during this latter decade that nuclear power generation is to gain dominance, reducing drastically the needed additions for the conventional fossil-fueled plants.[6]

Quantitatively, thermal efficiency is a function of time alone. This presents no estimation problem. To obtain a projected estimate of national average heat rates for fossil-fueled steam-electric plants (i.e., thermal efficiency) one inserts as the independent variable the actual year for which the estimate is desired. Once this estimate is secured, it can be inserted into the cost function for conventional fossil-fueled plants together with the net generation figure that has been forecast to obtain an estimate of the average annual production expense for the conventional fossil-fueled steam-electric plant. Note that the sequence involves two steps.

The actual annual production expenses and projected espenses for 1970 and 1975 through 1990 are presented in Table 5-1 for both hydroelectric and fossil-fueled steam-electric plants.

The projection of short-run average cost for nuclear steam-electric plants presents some special problems. A sample of only nine observations

Table 5-1
Annual Production Expenses: 1970-1990
(Mills per kWh)

Year	*Hydroelectric Plants*	*Fossil-Fueled Steam-Electric Plants*	*Nuclear Plants*
1970 (actual)	1.03	4.23	3.47
1975	0.88	3.20	2.54
1980	0.72	2.87	2.28
1985	0.70	2.64	2.09
1990	0.68	2.43	1.93

was used to estimate the coefficients on the average cost curve (equation (4.16)). Additionally, these observations are the first that are available since nuclear generation is a new phenomenon. Econometrically, one cannot question the estimates. The projected average cost for any year can be obtained by using an exogenous estimate of the independent variable, net generation. When this is obtained (using *Electrical World's* estimates as the source of the estimation of the change in net generation), the value that obtains for each of the years under consideration is unrealistically low. There are other estimates, principally by the Federal Power Commission, that, subjectively, are superior.[7] The problem that apparently has surfaced is that the forecast error is intolerably large due to the small sample size used in estimating the parameters of the cost equation. The variance of the forecast error consists of two parts, one equal to the variance of the disturbance and the other equal to the variance of the predictor (average cost) around its mean. The variance of the disturbance is beyond control, but the variance of the predictor can be diminished by increasing the size of the sample used for estimating the functional relation.[8] In the situation at hand, this is not feasible. One is left with the alternatives of either accepting the regression forecasts or seeking other estimates not based on such a projection technique. In consideration of the problems of forecast error and of the necessity to project twenty years with only a nine year time series, the latter course is selected. Note that these problems were not encountered with the projections for the hydroelectric and the conventional fossil-fueled plants because a much larger sample was used (for the period 1947-1970) and trends in plant operating factors have been well established, since the first plants date to around the turn of the century.

With these problems then, an eclectic method must be devised to project average variable cost for nuclear steam-electric generation. Since many of the factors affecting the behavior of the average cost of fossil-fueled steam-electric generation also affect the nuclear steam-electric generation (i.e., labor costs, plant operating supplies, and so on), the general trend of the fall in annual production expense is expected to be followed. The behavior of fuel costs is anticipated to be almost the same for each plant type.[9] However, operation and maintenance costs generally are related to kilowatts of installed capacity and for this reason are forecast to fall at a 3.3 percent faster rate for the nuclear plants than for a comparable conventional fossil plant.[10] The resultant projections are found in Table 5-1.

Projecting Capital Costs to 1990

The cost of building power facilities of a given size and type has been rising rapidly over the past few years because of increased land, labor, and materials cost and because of modifications for environmental reasons. This upward trend is expected to continue, although it is hoped that it can be slowed. Partially offsetting these facility cost rises will be the cost savings involved in the anticipated continued trend to larger generating units, and continuing improvements in technology and management.[11]

The estimation of capital cost is accomplished through the use of the CONCEPT package, as detailed in chapter 4. The input data will not override the assumptions that costs are referenced to the start of design and construction,[12] that there is a 40-hour work week with no overtime, that there is a constant 7 percent per year simple interest rate for calculating interest during construction, and that costs will escalate at a rate of one percent per year. It is assumed that the plant of specific interest will not differ significantly from the Atomic Energy Commission's (AEC) standard hypothetical description on these points. Additionally, the hypothetical reference plant is assumed to be located at the AEC's Middletown site. This site has an adequate supply of cooling water, a low population density, satisfactory transportation facilities, and a sufficient labor supply for a 40-hour workweek. By establishing the trends of the major cost components as a function of time, location, and plant type and size, the cost estimate for the hypothetical reference plant will be adjusted to fit the specific case of interest. Further, the reference plant size is 1000 megawatts and the reference year is 1970.

The input data stream that is needed to allow computation of the specific adjustments from the reference plant consists of plant electrical capacity, reactor type (or fossil-fuel type), plant location, and design and construction period.

During the first half of 1971, lead times for the construction of steam power plants were estimated at 4.5 to 5.5 years for fossil-fueled installations and at 7 to 7.5 years for nuclear units in the 800 to 1100 megawatt range. The key factor in a fossil schedule is fabrication and erection of the steam generator. For coal fired units, for example, the type of coal (larger boilers are required for poor coal), the shipping date, the location (a northern climate reduces the number of construction days during the winter), development of new sites (Difficult site preparation, construction of new roads and rail facilities add time.), environmental objections, and the national economy (Great amounts of construction in all industries puts designers and construction workers in high demand and generates labor problems.) all have an impact on the design and construction periods.[13]

Power industry problems over the past few years have affected fossil-fueled plant scheduling adversely. The sheer number of units has had a major impact. The rapid introduction of nuclear power affected their schedules because of the problems imposed on manufacturers, designers, and contractors. Environmental considerations can be more of a problem with fossil-fueled plants than with nuclear plants.[14] For nuclear plants streamlined licensing procedures and improved construction techniques may tend to shorten lead times, but other factors seem likely to lengthen them. As a result of the Calvert Cliffs court decision, additional requirements for environmental protection statements under the National Environmental Policy Act have added at least a year to construction lead times for nuclear plants. Greater public participation in the planning process may also lead to future delays.[15]

As a consequence, utilities planning on in-service dates of 1980, 1985, and so on will probably be obliged to commit themselves about 7.5 years earlier for nuclear plants. For fossil-fueled units on the other hand, commitments need only be made 5 years before scheduled operation. These are general considerations, and particular conditions could advance or retard the commitment time.[16]

The factors affecting hydroelectric plant construction lead times are much the same as those influencing fossil-fueled steam-electric plants. For example, the location of a particular site, capacity of the unit, and uses of automatic or remote supervisory control all influence the time needed for design and construction of a particular hydroelectric plant. It is expected that a 5 year commitment before scheduled operation is needed.[17]

The CONCEPT package bases its location calculations with regards to specific cities in a given region. With the realization there is a great deal of heterogeneity among cities in a region, what is done here is to select a city (of the 21 available sites) that is representative in economic and demographic terms of a region. The city selected determines which historical labor and material cost data are used. For determination of capital cost, the cities selected are Boston (New England), New York (Middle Atlantic), Chicago (East North Central), Kansas City (West North Central), Atlanta

(South Atlantic), Birmingham (East South Central), Dallas (West South Central), Denver (Mountain), and San Francisco (Pacific).

Within each general type of plant category, there are specific types of systems that can be selected. For example, for nuclear generation, various reactor concepts are divided generally into either "fast" or "thermal" classifications, depending on the energy of the neutrons initiating the fission process. Essentially all of the power reactors planned or in operation today are of the thermal type. In this category of thermal reactors, one finds the pressurized reactor system (PWR), the boiling water reactor (BWR), and the high temperature gas cooled reactor system (HTGR). The basic differences between these systems are the type and degree of uranium utilization and thermal efficiency. Because of limited production and experience, the HTGR has not reached the levels of technical development and commercial aceptance that have been achieved by the light water reactors (PWR and BWR).[18] In selecting one of the three types of nuclear thermal reactor systems as a basis on which to compute the capital cost, the PWR system is selected because, first, light water reactors are the best developed technologically at present of the available systems; second, projected capital costs over the period among regions differ (on the high side) from BWR by less than 2 percent; and third, there is still much uncertainty concerning important plant components and design requiring development and testing for the HTGR system.[19]

For conventional fossil-fueled steam-electric generation, one is confronted with three alternative and well developed plant types. The regional availability of fuel is the most significant determinant of the type of plant selected. Coal is the prime fuel in many parts of the nation. More and more western coal is burned from fields in Arizona and New Mexico northward to North Dakota and Montana. This coal, with its relatively low sulfur content, is desirable because it meets air pollution standards. In 1970, 57 percent of fossil-fueled steam-electric generation used coal as the fuel. Waterborne residual fuel oil is becoming an increasingly important fuel in new and conventional power plants along the Atlantic coast from Maine to Florida. Both natural gas and residual fuel oil are burned by Pacific Coast plants. Natural gas is the prime fuel in the West South Central region. Because of the growing gap between the national demand and supply of gas and the generally low priority given to the use of natural gas as a boiler fuel, it appears that less gas will be available for electrical energy generation in the years ahead. The percentage of energy generated in gas-fueled and oil-fueled plants in 1970 was 29 and 14 percent, respectively.[20]

If one were confronted with a differential in capital cost between these three types of conventional fossil-fueled plants, some weighting scheme would be appropriate and in fact would be desirable for each region based on the expected contribution of each plant type for the period under consideration. Fortunately however, the differential between each type is not appreciable, being under two percent.[21] Consequently, for expediting computations, coal will be used as the reference fuel for estimating capital cost for fossil-fueled steam-electric plants.

In considering hydroelectric power systems, one is confronted with estimating conventional and pumped storage plants' capital costs, which differ. The ratio of the conventional plant investment cost to the pumped storage cost is about 7 to 3. Further, megawatt additions for pumped storage plants are expected to be twice conventional capacity additions.[22] Given these and the aforementioned considerations concerning the use of the CONCEPT program to determine capital cost for a specific plant ("The Variable Costs—Hydroelectric Plants"—chapter 4), a coal plant with the appropriate multiplicative constant applied will be used to determine the capital cost figure for combined conventional and pumped storage plants.[23]

The last of the input data required is a specification of plant generating capacity. The most noteworthy development in recent years in generation units has been their increase in size and the accompanying progress in technology that has made these increases possible. Along with this increase in unit size has also come increases in plant size. The interest in larger units and plants, of course, stems from the utilities' desires to reduce per unit capital and operating costs. The availability of large blocks of power has had a significant impact on system planning, design, and operation. It is expected that the trend to increasing unit sizes will continue because of the expected per unit decline in cost with increasing size.

In a report of the Technical Advisory Committee on Generation to the Federal Power Commission, particular attention was given to the unit sizes that may be installed for fossil-fueled and nuclear plant capacity. Acknowledging the direct effect of unit size on capital cost and economy of generation, there tends to be an increase in required reserve capacity with larger unit sizes. In addition balancing the economy of size with the cost of additional reserves, there are other factors that must be considered in selecting the optimum unit size for installation at a particular time and place. These include manufacturing limitations, load growth, load concentrations, environmental considerations, and transmission needs.

Taking account of all of these considerations with the accompanying qualifications, the Committee has estimated the composition of the 1980 and 1990 fossil-fueled and nuclear steam-electric capacity. For fossil-fueled plants, units in the 1000 megawatt range are expected to account for about 90 percent of all additions between 1970 and 1980 and for about 50 percent of all additions between 1980 and 1990 for sizes up to 3000 megawatts. For nuclear plants, units in the 1000 megawatt range are expected to account for about 80 percent of new capacity between 1970 and 1980 and for about 50 percent of new capacity between 1980 and 1990 for sizes up to 3000 megawatts.[24] Therefore, for both nuclear steam-electric and fossil-fueled steam-electric plants, plant generating capacity is assumed to be 1000 megawatts.

Hydroelectric developments, being dependent on dams and waterways to harness the energy of falling water to produce electrical energy, are approaching the size of steam-electric plants. The current trend toward construction of very large nuclear and fossil-fueled steam: electric units that operate best at high plant capacity factors has increased the need for plants designed specifically for peak load operation. This has led to the construction of pumped storage and other hydroelectric plants with large generation capacity designed for low plant capacity factor operation.

Generating units are being constructed in increasingly larger sizes. The trend to larger hydroelectric plants and units is likely to continue, with possible savings in both capital and operation costs. Improvements in the design and construction of dams are contributing to the economies of hydroelectric power developments. Also contributing to such economies are advances in the techniques and equipment used in tunneling and other underground excavation.

The Federal Power Commission staff has made a study on locations of projected new conventional and pumped storage projects and capacity additions between 1970 and 1990. This study examined project construction and associated transmission costs, energy losses in pumping and transmission for pumped storage units, and environmental and aesthetic considerations. The average generating capacity is about 1000 megawatts for the period.[25] Consequently, the capital cost estimate will be based on a unit with this capacity.

For all of these input specifications, the CONCEPT program was allowed to estimate the cost per kilowatt of generating capacity. The computations are in constant 1970 dollars. The estimated cost for each region and plant type is found in Table 5-2.

Given these capital cost estimates, one can determine the per unit (kWh) investment costs. This calculation is straight forward, being based on the service life of the particular plant type, the total net generation expected each year, the rate of capital equipment depreciation, and the annual rate of fixed charges, which include the cost of money, interim replacements, insurance, and taxes.

These annual fixed charges are all related to investment in plant in service and are expressed on a levelized basis as a percentage of the investment. The percentage relationships vary with ownership segments—privately owned, federal, municipal, and cooperative. Annual fixed charge rates also vary by plant type, primarily because of differences in service lives but also because of some difference in tax rates and other items. These fixed charge rates are calculated for each plant type and vary

Table 5-2
Capital Cost by Plant Type for Electrical Energy Generation: 1970-1990
(Dollars per Kilowatt)

Region	*Year*	*Hydroelectric Plants*	*Fossil-fueled Plants*	*Nuclear Plants*
1. New England	1970	$287	$258	$289
	1975	300	270	302
	1980	315	283	316
	1985	330	297	331
	1990	346	311	346
2. Middle Atlantic	1970	311	280	312
	1975	325	293	326
	1980	341	307	341
	1985	357	322	357
	1990	375	337	374
3. East North Central	1970	285	256	287
	1975	298	268	300
	1980	312	281	314
	1985	327	294	329
	1990	343	309	344
4. West North Central	1970	330	259	289
	1975	345	271	303
	1980	362	284	317
	1985	379	298	332
	1990	397	312	347
5. South Atlantic	1970	284	242	272
	1975	297	254	285
	1980	311	266	298
	1985	326	278	312
	1990	341	291	326
6. East South Central	1970	270	231	260
	1975	283	241	272
	1980	296	253	285
	1985	310	265	298
	1990	325	277	312
7. West South Central	1970	299	235	265
	1975	313	246	277
	1980	328	257	289
	1985	343	269	303
	1990	360	282	317
8. Mountain	1970	290	241	271
	1975	304	252	283
	1980	318	264	297
	1985	333	277	310
	1990	349	290	325
9. Pacific	1970	322	267	299
	1975	337	280	313
	1980	353	294	328
	1985	370	308	343
	1990	388	322	359

regionally between 6.5 percent and 14.3 percent for hydroelectric plants, between 12.7 percent and 15.4 percent for fossil-fueled plants, and between 13.2 percent and 15.6 percent for nuclear plants.[26]

The service life for the various plant types are as follows: for nuclear and fossil-fueled plants, 30 years; for hydroelectric plants, 50 years.[27] The rate of capital depreciation is discussed in the following section.

The total net generation expected from each plant type in any given year is computed on the basis of a capital-output coefficient, with the inverse of this coefficient giving the net generation per unit of capital, where both capital and output are measured over the same time period. The computation of a capital-output coefficient for electrical energy has generated some controversy mainly because of the search for an appropriate definition of capital. This problem is encountered in most studies of production.[28] The definition of capital used is so designed as to be consistent with the problem under investigation. The definition employed here will be no different. Capital is measured in terms of kilowatts and not in dollar terms.[29] This is accomplished simply by using installed generating capacity as the measure.

To get an accurate measure of the capital-output coefficient, average net generation and average installed generating capacity for the eleven year period 1960 through 1970 are used. The average is used since additions to generating capacity come in large lumps and the use of any one year values will tend to bias the estimate of the coefficient. It is interesting to note the stability of the coefficient by region and for hydroelectric and fossil-fueled steam-electric plants over the period. The calculations can be performed using the data from the *Statistical Yearbook* (various years) of the Edison Electric Institute for hydroelectric and fossil-fueled steam-electric plants.

The nuclear capital-output coefficient involves special considerations. Only four out of nine regions had any appreciable generation of electrical energy from nuclear plants between 1960 and 1970. Additionally, many technological and operational problems have been encountered in the plants in service, necessitating a substantial amount of downtime (forced outage) to alleviate or correct the problem so that the capital-output coefficient is not at all representative of operation under normal conditions. It is suggested then that to compute the capital-output coefficient, an indirect technique be used.

The indirect technique is to use the capacity factor estimate for nuclear plants. The capacity factor measures the energy actually produced during a specified period, as a fraction of the energy that could have been produced, and therefore is a measure of idle capacity. As the capacity factor becomes less, for example, a smaller portion of the energy producing potential is utilized, so that the investment in capacity is not earning all that it could. Specifically, annual capacity factor is defined to equal annual energy produced in kWh divided by the product of the number of hours in a year and total installed capacity in kilowatts, the latter taken to be constant throughout the year. By multiplying this capacity factor by the number of hours in a year, one obtains the capital-output coefficient.

It is usually assumed that new plants have a capacity factor of 80 percent.[30] However, Philip Sporn, former president of the American Electric Power Company, has noted that with the growth of atomic power, no nuclear plant can, except for the shortest time, be expected to operate at a capacity factor as high as 80 percent and that a more rational capacity factor is 75 percent.[31] This compares to a capacity factor averaging about 51 percent for hydroelectric plants and about 52 percent for conventional steam-electric plants. Because only a national capacity factor is available, it will be assumed that a nuclear unit in any one region will operate with the same capacity factor as a nuclear unit in any other region and hence with the same capital-output coefficient. The annual capital-output coefficient is 6570 kWh/kW.

The Regional Reliability Councils of the Federal Power Commission have projected capacity factors (which differ from the capital-output coefficients by a multiplicative constant) to 1995. These capacity factor projections for each region are remarkably stable.[32] Hence, it will be assumed that the regional capital-output coefficients are time-invariant.

Supply Constraints: Empirical Values

In chapter 4 where the cost minimization problem was considered, certain constraints were noted that affect the supply side of the model. Empirical values for the relevant parameters and the method of obtaining estimates of the capacity constraints will be presented in this section.

The projections for addition limitations to generating capacity for various plant types will be taken from *The 1970 National Power Survey*. Note that the power supply regional breakdown in this survey does not correspond perfectly to the regional definition being employed here. However, the correspondence is close enough so that looking at percentage net addition over the period for various plant types, one can obtain a good estimate of additional capacity limitations. The net new capacity needs is used as an effective constraint because energy resources available to individual regions are largely reflected in these estimates.[33] For example, because of a large underdeveloped capacity, the Pacific region will install the bulk of new conventional hydroelectric capacity with the only constraint on the installation being its engineering feasibility.[34] There is expected to be a pronounced expansion of nuclear generating capacity and an increasing reliance on nuclear plants, relative to total generation, over the next two decades. Further, the addition to capacity in the initial period is constrained to be zero for the reason discussed in chapter 6.

There is one parameter that must be determined in equation (4.6): r_Θ, the rate of capital depreciation. The depreciation rates are obtained from a Federal Power Commission survey of annual reports for companies accounting for virtually all investment and revenue of the privately owned sector of the electrical energy industry. Overall depreciation rates of electric utility companies differ considerably because of the varying service lives of different classes of generating equipment and the different proportions of each type operated by individual companies. For this reason one finds extremes in the depreciation rates used by individual companies. To mitigate the problem of getting an unrepresentative average rate of depreciation, the median value for each plant type is selected. The annual rates of depreciation for the various generating plants are as follows: fossil-fueled steam-electric generation, 2.95 percent; hydroelectric generation, 1.52 percent; and nuclear steam-electric generation, 5.0 percent.[35]

As an aside, it might be noted that the reason the depreciation rate is applied to the existing capacity for each of the periods of consideration is to take account of wear and tear, decay, action of the elements, obsolescence, changes in the technology, changes in demand, and requirements of public authorities.

As a final comment on these empirical estimates and the flows of electrical energy generated, note that all of the values are in net terms. Approximately ten percent of the electrical energy generated is lost in transmission with the actual percentage loss variable across regions depending on the age and type of equipment being used. To get total figures, it would simply be necessary to inflate the net generation figures by the appropriate percentage losses.

6 An Intertemporal-Spatial Price Equilibrium Model

Development planning is a continuous and sequential process involving mobilization and efficient use of resources. In this context the important aspect of development planning in the electrical energy sector is the formulation of suitable policies to carry out the economic activities of the generation, transmission and distribution, and consumption over time and over space of electrical energy. Thus, the problem posed here is to develop a planning model that will yield an efficient solution with regard to consumption, generation, and pricing over space for each of the time periods over the operative planning period. Within the confines of this model, it will then be shown quantitatively that opportunities exist for increasing the efficiency of pricing and allocating electrical energy in the United States if a departure from past policy is undertaken. This chapter is devoted to developing the theoretical formulation of such a model and providing an empirical solution, with the subsequent chapter devoted to looking at policy implications and to providing a conclusion to the study.

Overview

As a basis for the specification to follow, the problem of equilibrium among spatially separated markets is couched in terms of descriptive price behavior, which is converted to a maximization problem concerned with maximizing net social payoff (*NSP*). Net social payoff in terms of the underlying supply and demand relations for all regions is defined as follows: The sum of the areas under the demand functions less the sum of the areas under the supply functions at posttrade equilibrium prices, minus the sum of the areas under the demand functions less the sum of the areas under the supply functions at pretrade prices, minus the total transmission and distribution costs incurred. Because the sum of the areas under the demand functions less the sum of the areas under the supply functions at pretrade prices is constant, the sum may be omitted from the definition without altering the posttrade prices and allocation.

By noting that many economic relations in time have many of the properties of economic relations in space, the tools for analyzing spatial competitive relations can be applied to the more complex problem of equilibrium pricing and allocation of electrical energy over time.

Combining the temporal and spatial aspects of the problem, the concept of net social payoff is used as a basis for deducing the conditions of spatial and intertemporal equilibrium. The peculiarities of an intertemporal-spatial model[1] and of the electrical energy industry are incorporated into a model that can be solved directly for a competitive solution. Introducing the time dimension into the model opens the way to handling many of the knotty problems concerned with investment in capital equipment as well as the problems involved with price adjustment and allocation over time when one region gains an economic advantage in the generation of electrical energy or possesses a rapidly growing demand for electrical energy that cannot be met solely on the basis of intraregional capacity.

The Economic Environment

In this chapter the same notation and definitions that are employed in the previous chapters are used. For convenience, the notation and definitions are restated as follows: let

i, j where $i, j = 1, 2, \ldots, N(M)$ denote the regions (or consuming sectors),

Θ where $\Theta = 1, 2, \ldots, L$ denote the plant type for generating electrical energy,

t, τ for $t, \tau = 1, 2, \ldots, T$ denote the discrete time period (in five year increments)[2],

y_{ijt} for all i, j, and t denote the quantity of electrical energy demanded by the ith sector in the jth region in the tth period,

x_{ijt} for all i, j, and t denote the quantity of electrical energy transmitted interregionally (for $i \neq j$) and distributed intraregionally ($i = j$) in period t,

x^{Θ}_{jt} for all Θ, j and t denote the net quantity of electrical energy generated in region j by plant type Θ in period t,

$\tilde{x}^{\Theta}_{jt}$ for all Θ, j, and t denote the maximum net quantity of electrical energy that can be generated in region j by plant type Θ in period t,

W^{Θ}_{jt} for all Θ, j, and t denote the investment in capacity of each plant type that will be added in the current period t,[3]

$\tilde{W}^{\Theta}_{jt}$ for all j and t, and Θ denote the maximum investment in capacity that can be added in the current period t in region j for plant type Θ,

S_{j1}^{Θ} for all Θ and j denote the generating capacity of plant type Θ existing in region j in period 1,

Pe_{ijt} for all i, j, and t denote the demand price on the ith sector in the jth region in the tth period,

Pe_t^j for all j and t denote the supply price in the jth region in the tth period,

f_{ijt} for all i, j, and t denote the distribution charge per kWh of electrical energy generated in region i and distributed to region j in period t,

c_{ijt}^* for all i, j, and t denote the marginal cost of transmitting one unit (kWh) of electrical energy from region i to region j in period t,

Ψ_{jt}^{Θ} for all Θ, j, and t denote the marginal cost of operating a plant of type Θ in region j in period t,

ξ_{jt}^{Θ} for all Θ, j, and t denote the marginal cost of adding one kilowatt-hour to capacity of plant type Θ in region j in period t, and

Pe_{jt}^{Θ} for all Θ, j, and t denote the capital cost of generating an additional kilowatt-hour of electrical energy for plant type Θ in region j in period t.

For each region the demand functions are given in the following form:

$$Pe_{jt} = \begin{bmatrix} Pe_{1jt} \\ \vdots \\ Pe_{Mjt} \end{bmatrix} = \begin{bmatrix} \lambda_{1jt} \\ \vdots \\ \lambda_{Mjt} \end{bmatrix} - \begin{bmatrix} \omega_{1jt} & 0 & \cdots & 0 \\ & & & \\ 0 & \cdots & & \omega_{mjt} \end{bmatrix} \begin{bmatrix} y_{1jt} \\ \vdots \\ y_{Mjt} \end{bmatrix} \tag{6.1a}$$

$$= \lambda_{jt} - \Omega_{jt}\, y_{jt}^*$$

or

$$y_{jt}^* = \begin{bmatrix} y_{1jt} \\ \vdots \\ y_{Mjt} \end{bmatrix} = \begin{bmatrix} \alpha_{1jt} \\ \vdots \\ \alpha_{Mjt} \end{bmatrix} - \begin{bmatrix} \beta_{1jt} & 0 & \cdots & 0 \\ & & & \\ 0 & \cdots & & \beta_{Mjt} \end{bmatrix} \begin{bmatrix} Pe_{1jt} \\ \vdots \\ Pe_{Mjt} \end{bmatrix} \tag{6.1b}$$

$$= \alpha_{jt} - \beta_{jt}\, Pe_{jt}$$

$$\lambda_{jt} = \beta_{jt}^{-1}\alpha_{jt} \tag{6.1c}$$

$$\Omega_{jt} = \beta_{jt}^{-1} \text{ for all } j \text{ and } t.$$

For each region the short-run cost functions are given in the following form:

$$Z_{jt} = \begin{bmatrix} \Psi^1_{jt} \\ \vdots \\ \Psi^L_{jt} \end{bmatrix} \text{ for } \begin{bmatrix} x^1_{jt} \\ \vdots \\ x^L_{jt} \end{bmatrix} < \begin{bmatrix} \tilde{x}^1_{jt} \\ \vdots \\ \tilde{x}^L_{jt} \end{bmatrix} \tag{6.2a}$$

$$= \Psi_{jt} \text{ for } x^*_{jt} < \tilde{x}_{jt} \text{ for all } \Theta, j, \text{ and } t.$$

If equality between x_{jt} and $\tilde{x}_{jt}$ holds, then the short-run price will be determined by the Lagrangian (see equation (6.10)).

For each region the cost function for additional capacity is given in the following form:

$$R_{jt} = \begin{bmatrix} \xi^1_{jt} \\ \vdots \\ \xi^L_{jt} \end{bmatrix} \text{ for all } \Theta, j, \text{ and } t. \tag{6.2b}$$

Assumption (1): β_{jt} is symmetric and positive definite, and all elements of Z_{jt} and R_{jt} are positive for all Θ, j, and t.

For each region and each time period, the total quantity of electrical energy actually consumed must be less than or equal to the quantity supplied by that region plus the quantity transmitted from other regions:

$$y_{jt} \leq \sum_i x_{ijt}, \text{ for all } i, j, \text{ and } t \tag{6.3}$$

where the total quantity of electrical energy actually consumed is the sum of the quantities consumed by each of the sectors:

$$y_{jt} = \sum_i y_{ijt}, \text{ for all } i, j, \text{ and } t. \tag{6.4}$$

For each region and each plant type and each time period, the total net generation of electrical energy is less than or equal to the net generation from each plant type:

$$\sum_i x_{jit} \leq \sum_\Theta x^\Theta_{jt}, \text{ for all } \Theta, j, \text{ and } t. \tag{6.5}$$

For each plant type in each region for each time period, net generation is less than or equal to the net generation from that plant type existing in the first period (depreciated appropriately) plus the generation from the capacity of the given plant type added in the first and subsequent periods:

$$x_{jt}^{\Theta} \leq \sigma_{\Theta}^{t-1} S_{j1}^{\Theta} + \sum_{\tau=1}^{t} \sigma_{\Theta}^{t-\tau} W_{j\tau}^{\Theta} \tag{6.6}$$

for all Θ, j, t and $\sigma_{\Theta}^{t-\tau} = \dfrac{1}{(1 + r^{\Theta})^{t-\tau}}$

Finally, for each plant type specifically considered (i.e., hydroelectric, fossil-fueled, and nuclear), in all regions in each time period, investment in new generating capacity is constrained by physical, institutional, and technological limitations:

$$W_{jt}^{\Theta} \leq \tilde{W}_{jt}^{\Theta}, \text{ for all } \Theta, j, \text{ and } t; \tag{6.7}$$

While this limitation is self-evident for hydroelectric generation, one might question it for nuclear plants and fossil-fueled plants. However, there is adequate recognition that there is a maximum feasible expansion say in nuclear power development considering the limitations presently imposed by specific factors such as licensing, development of additional uranium supplies, technical and construction manpower limitations, difficulties with new and extrapolated equipment, and so on.[4] For fossil-fueled plants, similar considerations hold.[5]

Given that the problem is marked at an initial point of reference (i.e., $t = 1$), it is assumed that capacity cannot be added instantaneously, so that only capacity existing in this initial period is available to meet demand. Consequently, net additions to capacity are constrained to be less than or equal to zero in the first period:

$$W_{j1}^{\Theta} \leq 0, \text{ for all } \Theta \text{ and } j. \tag{6.7a}$$

If future welfare is looked upon as discountable or commensurable with present welfare through a common time discount factor, say $\sigma^{t-1} = 1/(1 + r^{d})^{t-1}$, for $t = 1, 2, \ldots, T$ with r^d being the social rate of discount, the following discounting convention can be used: let

$$NSP = NSP(1) + \sigma NSP(2) + \ldots + \sigma^{T-1} NSP(T) \tag{6.8}$$

where NSP and $NSP(t)$, for all t, stand for the total discounted net social payoff and undiscounted net social payoff measured at the tth period.

This entire notion of discounting future periods' welfare dates back to F. P. Ramsey. It was his argument that it is ethically indefensible not to discount later welfare (or enjoyment in his words) with earlier welfare, and not doing so arises merely from the weakness of the imagination.[6] However, opposition to such discounting extends beyond this weakness of imagination. Surely if one took an egalitarian approach to the problem under study where future periods' welfare is considered identical in value to the present period's welfare, the discount factor would be set equal to zero, assuming of course the future is foreseeable and foreseen.

The reason for discounting, it is argued, is that decisions about current allocations must be made in the presence of uncertainty and perhaps all one should ask of the model is that it focus on current decisions and indicate prospective plans for future allocations, taking into account the best possible estimate of future conditions.[7] The model can then be used sequentially to reconsider plans made for future allocations as more information is acquired and a clearer picture is obtained of the demand and supply relations for each period. Hence, in an effort to make the best possible current decisions in every period on the current valuation of total net social payoff for the present and future periods, the discounted value of future payoffs are aggregated with the present value of the current period's payoff. Through the discounting procedure, one is taking account of the uncertainty of the future as well as forcing any infinite time period consideration (i.e., if T were allowed to approach infinity) to essentially one of finite time periods since payoffs after some future point in time would have negligible present value. If one assumes a high degree of certainty prevails for all relevant time periods and if the span of the time horizon is short, discounting may not be desirable.

The choice of an appropriate social rate of discount is a difficult task with a voluminous literature surrounding the considerations. These are nicely summarized by Prest and Turvey.[8] The concepts of social rate of time preference, social opportunity cost, and adjustment for uncertainty serve as the basis for selecting an appropriate social rate of discount. Practically, the most usual procedure is to select an interest rate on the basis of observed rates ruling at the time when computing present value.[9] There is no uniquely superior way of selecting a social rate of discount and for this reason more than a single rate can be considered.

Definition of Intertemporal-Spatial Equilibrium

Given this economic environment, one is now in a position to define an intertemporal-spatial equilibrium.

An economy $(\bar{y}_{ijt}, \bar{x}_{jt}^{\Theta}, \bar{x}_{ijt}, \bar{W}_{jt}^{\Theta})$, for all Θ, i, j, and t as defined above is said to be in an intertemporal-spatial equilibrium if the following conditions are fulfilled:

(a) homogeneity and uniqueness of market price for electrical energy in a region during any time period. (This means that the price in a given region paid by each consuming sector is the same.);

(b) no excess demand for electrical energy in any region during any time period,

$$\bar{e}_{jt} = \sum_i \bar{x}_{ijt} - \sum_i \bar{y}_{ijt} \geq 0$$

and efficient market pricing (demand):

$$\bar{e}_{jt}\ \overline{Pe}_{jt} = 0 \text{ for all } j \text{ and } t;$$

(c) excess supply possible for electrical energy in any region at any time period,

$$\bar{e}^j_t = \sum_\Theta \bar{x}^\Theta_{jt} - \sum_i \bar{x}_{jit} \geq 0$$

and efficient market pricing (supply),

$$\bar{e}^j_t \overline{Pe}^j_t = 0, \text{ for all } j \text{ and } t;$$

d) spatial price equilibrium,

$$\bar{e}_{ijt} = \overline{Pe}_{jt} - \overline{Pe}^i_t - f_{ijt} - c^*_{ijt} \leq 0$$

and

$$\bar{e}_{ijt}\ \bar{x}_{ijt} = 0, \text{ for all } i, j, \text{ and } t;$$

(e) equilibrium price for alternative methods of generating electrical energy,

$$\bar{e}^\Theta_{jt} = \overline{Pe}^j_t - \Psi^\Theta_{jt} - \overline{Pe}^\Theta_{jt} \leq 0$$

and

$$\bar{e}^\Theta_{jt}\bar{x}^\Theta_{jt} = 0, \text{ for all } \Theta, j, \text{ and } t;$$

(f) equilibrium price for additions to capacity,

$$\bar{e}^\Theta_{jt} = \overline{Pe}^\Theta_{jt} - \xi^\Theta_{jt} - \overline{Pe}^{\Theta *}_{jt} \leq 0$$

and

$$\bar{e}^\Theta_{jt}\overline{W}^\Theta_{jt} = 0, \text{ for all } \Theta, j, \text{ and } t.$$

$Pe^{\Theta *}_{jt}$ is the cost society must incur for not being able to expand plant capacity of type Θ^* beyond a particular limit.

Condition (a) is the usual price condition for a competitive equilibrium and does not require any explanation here.

Condition (b) states that if consumption of electrical energy in region j during period t is exactly equal to the quantity inflow from all regions during period t, the market demand price can be positive, while if the consumption is less than the inflow, the market demand price must be zero in period t.

Condition (c) states that if generation of electrical energy in region j exceeds transmissions from that region to all regions, the market supply price of electrical energy must be zero, and if the former is exactly exhausted by the latter, the market supply price can be positive.

Condition (d) is a typical spatial price equilibrium condition and an interpretation need not be given here.

Condition (e) states that if generation of electrical energy in region j from a particular plant type exceeds zero, the supply price is equal to the operating cost and investment cost of each plant type. If no electrical energy is generated by a particular type of plant, then necessarily, the supply price is less than or equal to operating and investment costs.

Condition (f) states that if there is a net addition to capacity of plant type Θ, the price of that addition is equal to the marginal cost of investment plus the penalty society incurs for being constrained to this plant type in region j for time period t. Note that if there is no constraint on the addition to capacity of a particular plant type, the penalty incurred will be zero.

The definition thus combines two price equilibria: a spatial price equilibrium and an investment price equilibrium (intertemporal equilibrium). In the following section, a mathematical programming model will be constructed, and it will be shown that the model once solved satisfies all the conditions stipulated in this definition.

Mathematical Formulation

One can now form the total discounted net quasi-welfare function for the intertemporal-spatial model in the following form:

$$NSP = \sum_t \sigma^{t-1} \Big[\sum_i \sum_j \int (\lambda_{ijt} - \omega_{ijt}\, y_{ijt})\, dy_{ijt} \tag{6.9}$$

$$- \sum_i \sum_j f_{ijt}\, x_{ijt} - \sum_i \sum_j c^*_{ijt}\, x_{ijt}$$

$$- \sum_j \sum_\Theta \Psi^\Theta_{jt}\, x^\Theta_{jt} - \sum_j \sum_\Theta \xi^\Theta_{jt}\, W^\Theta_{jt} \Big]$$

Given the economic environment and the objective function (6.9), the formulation of the mathematical programming problem is as follows:

Find $\bar{\chi}_{ijt} = (\bar{y}_{ijt}, \bar{x}_{ijt}, \bar{x}^\Theta_{jt}, \bar{W}^\Theta_{jt})$ for all $\Theta = 1, 2, \ldots, L$, $i, j = 1, 2, \ldots, N(M)$, and $t = 1, 2, \ldots, T$ that maximizes (6.9) subject to the constraint set (6.3) through (6.7a) and $y_{ijt} \geq 0$, $x_{ijt} \geq 0$, $x^\Theta_{jt} \geq 0$, and $W^\Theta_{jt} \geq 0$.

The net benefit function (6.9) is a concave function in χ^{Θ}_{ijt} for all Θ, i, j, and t by assumption (1) and the constraint set satisfies Slater's condition.[10] By the equivalence theorem,[11] the solution set χ^{Θ}_{ijt} for all Θ, i, j, and t is the part of a saddle point (χ, ρ) of the following saddle value problem:

find a saddle point of the Lagrangian

$$\begin{aligned} \Phi(\chi\ \rho) = & \sum_t \sigma^{t-1} \Bigg(\sum_i \sum_J \lambda_{ijt} y_{ijt} - \tfrac{1}{2}\omega_{ijt}\, y^2_{ijt} \\ & - \sum_i \sum_j f_{ijt} x_{ijt} - \sum_i \sum_j c^*_{ijt}\, x_{ijt} \\ & - \sum_j \sum_\Theta \Psi^{\Theta}_{jt} x^{\Theta}_{jt} - \sum_j \sum_\Theta \xi^{\Theta}_{jt} W^{\Theta}_{jt} \Bigg) \\ & + \sum_t \sigma^{t-1} \sum_j \Bigg[\rho^1_{jt} \Bigg(\sum_i x_{ijt} - \sum_i y_{ijt} \Bigg) \\ & + \rho^2_{jt} \Bigg(\sum_\Theta x^{\Theta}_{jt} - \sum_i x_{jit} \Bigg) \\ & + \sum_\Theta \rho^{\Theta}_{jt} \Bigg(\sigma^{t-1}_{\Theta} S^{\Theta}_{j1} + \sum_{\tau=1}^{t} \sigma^{t-\tau}_{\Theta}\, W^{\Theta}_{j\tau} - x^{\Theta}_{jt} \Bigg) \\ & + \sum_{\Theta^*} \rho^{\Theta^*}_{jt} \Big(\tilde{W}^{\Theta^*}_{jt} - W^{\Theta^*}_{jt} \Big) \Bigg]. \end{aligned} \tag{6.10}$$

where $\Theta^* = 1, 2, \ldots, L$ consists of the plant types for which there is a capacity limitation. Note that if a plant type were introduced that did not possess a capacity limitation, the $\rho^{\Theta^*}_{jt}$ would simply be zero.

Optimality Conditions

The Kuhn-Tucker conditions for optimality for (6.10) are as follows:[12]

$$\begin{aligned} \frac{\partial \overline{\Phi}}{\partial y_{ijt}} &= \sigma^{t-1} (\lambda_{ijt} - \omega_{ijt} \overline{y}_{ijt}) - \sigma^{t-1} \overline{\rho}^1_{jt} \leq 0 \\ &= \sigma^{t-1} \overline{Pe}_{ijt} - \sigma^{t-1} \overline{\rho}^1_{jt} \leq 0 \end{aligned} \tag{6.11}$$

or simply

$$\overline{Pe}_{ijt} - \overline{\rho}^1_{jt} \leq 0$$

and

$$\frac{\partial \overline{\Phi}}{\partial y_{ijt}}\, \overline{y}_{ijt} = 0, \text{ for all } i, j, \text{ and } t;$$

$$\frac{\partial \overline{\Phi}}{\partial x_{ijt}} = -\sigma^{t-1} f_{ijt} \quad - \sigma^{t-1} c^{*}_{ijt} \quad + \sigma^{t-1} \overline{\rho}^{1}_{jt} \quad - \sigma^{t-1} \overline{\rho}^{2}_{it} \leq 0 \qquad (6.12)$$

or simply

$$-f_{ijt} - c^{*}_{ijt} \quad + \overline{\rho}^{1}_{jt} - \overline{\rho}^{2}_{it} \leq 0$$

and

$$\frac{\partial \overline{\Phi}}{\partial x_{ijt}} \overline{x}_{ijt} = 0, \text{ for all } i, j, \text{ and } t;$$

$$\frac{\partial \overline{\Phi}}{\partial x^{\Theta}_{jt}} = -\sigma^{t-1} \Psi^{\Theta}_{jt} \quad + \sigma^{t-1} \overline{\rho}^{2}_{jt} \quad - \sigma^{t-1} \overline{\rho}^{\Theta}_{jt} \leq 0 \qquad (6.13)$$

or simply,

$$-\Psi^{\Theta}_{jt} \quad + \overline{\rho}^{2}_{jt} \; - \overline{\rho}^{\Theta}_{jt} \leq 0$$

and

$$\frac{\partial \overline{\Phi}}{\partial x^{\Theta}_{jt}} \overline{x}^{\Theta}_{jt} = 0, \text{ for all } \Theta, j, \text{ and } t;$$

$$\frac{\partial \overline{\Phi}}{\partial W^{\Theta}_{jt}} = -\sigma^{t-1} \xi^{\Theta}_{jt} + \sigma^{t-1} \overline{\rho}^{\Theta}_{jt} - \sigma^{t-1} \overline{\rho}^{\Theta *}_{jt} \leq 0 \qquad (6.14)$$

or simply

$$-\xi^{\Theta}_{jt} \quad + \overline{\rho}^{\Theta}_{jt} \; - \overline{\rho}^{\Theta *}_{jt} \leq 0$$

and

$$\frac{\partial \overline{\Phi}}{\partial W^{\Theta}_{jt}} \overline{W}^{\Theta}_{jt} = 0, \text{ for all } \Theta, j, \text{ and } t;$$

$$\frac{\partial \overline{\Phi}}{\partial \rho^{1}_{jt}} = \sigma^{t-1} \left(\sum_{i} \overline{x}_{ijt} - \sum_{i} \overline{y}_{ijt} \right) \geq 0 \qquad (6.15)$$

or

$$\sum_{i} \overline{x}_{ijt} - \sum_{i} \overline{y}_{ijt} \geq 0$$

and

$$\frac{\partial \overline{\Phi}}{\partial \rho^{1}_{jt}} \quad \overline{\rho}^{1}_{jt} \quad = 0, \text{ for all } j \text{ and } t;$$

$$\frac{\partial \overline{\Phi}}{\partial \rho^{2}_{jt}} = \sigma^{t-1} \left(\sum_{\Theta} \overline{x}^{\Theta}_{jt} - \sum_{i} \overline{x}_{jit} \right) \geq 0 \qquad (6.16)$$

or

$$\sum_{\Theta} \bar{x}_{jt}^{\Theta} - \sum_{i} \bar{x}_{jit} \geq 0$$

and

$$\frac{\partial \bar{\Phi}}{\partial \rho_{jt}^{2}} \; \bar{\rho}_{jt}^{2} \; = 0, \text{for all } j \text{ and } t;$$

$$\frac{\partial \bar{\Phi}}{\partial \rho_{jt}^{\Theta}} = \sigma^{t-1}(\sigma_{\Theta}^{t-1} S_{j1}^{\Theta} + \sum_{\tau=1}^{t} \sigma_{\Theta}^{t-\tau} \bar{W}_{jt}^{\Theta} - \bar{x}_{jt}^{\Theta}) \geq 0 \tag{6.17}$$

or

$$\sigma_{\Theta}^{t-1} S_{j1}^{\Theta} + \sum_{\tau=1}^{t} \sigma_{\Theta}^{t-\tau} \bar{W}_{jt} - \bar{x}_{jt}^{\Theta} \geq 0$$

and

$$\frac{\partial \bar{\Phi}}{\partial \rho_{jt}^{\Theta}} \bar{\rho}_{jt}^{\Theta} = 0, \text{ for all } \Theta, j, \text{ and } t;$$

$$\frac{\partial \bar{\Phi}}{\partial \rho_{jt}^{\Theta *}} = \sigma^{t-1}(\tilde{W}_{jt}^{\Theta} - \bar{W}_{jt}^{\Theta}) \geq 0 \tag{6.18}$$

or

$$(\tilde{W}_{jt}^{\Theta} - \bar{W}_{jt}^{\Theta}) \geq 0$$

and

$$\frac{\partial \bar{\Phi}}{\partial \rho_{jt}^{\Theta *}} \bar{\rho}_{jt}^{\Theta *} = 0, \text{ for all } \Theta^*, j, \text{ and } t.$$

Condition (6.11) states that when demand is positive, say $\bar{y}_{ijt} > 0$, the discounted demand price $\sigma^{t-1}\overline{Pe}_{ijt}$ must be exactly equal to the discounted market demand price prevailing across sectors in a given region and for a given time period. When $\bar{y}_{ijt} = 0$, the discounted demand price is either less than or equal to the discounted market demand price for each sector, region, and time period. Alternately, when the optimal demand is positive, the demand price must be exactly equal to the market demand price and when the optimal demand is zero, the demand price is either less than or equal to the market demand price for each sector in each region and for each time period. Thus,

$$\text{if } \bar{y}_{ijt} > 0, \; \lambda_{ijt} - \omega_{ijt}\bar{y}_{ijt} = \overline{Pe}_{ijt} = \bar{\rho}_{jt}^{1} \; (\geq 0) \tag{6.19}$$

and

$$\text{if } \bar{y}_{ijt} = 0, \; \lambda_{ijt} - \omega_{ijt}\bar{y}_{ijt} = \overline{Pe}_{ijt} \leq \bar{\rho}_{jt}^{1} \; (\geq 0).$$

Condition (6.12) states that when the optimal flow $\bar{x}_{ijt}$ is positive, the difference between the discounted market demand and discounted market supply prices, $\sigma^{t-1}(\bar{\rho}^1_{jt} - \bar{\rho}^2_{it})$ is equal to the discounted interregional transmission cost plus distribution cost $\sigma^{t-1}(f_{ijt} + c^*_{ijt})$ and if $\bar{x}_{ijt} = 0$, the difference is less than or equal to the sum of these two costs. Stated differently, when the optimal flow is positive, the difference between the market demand and market supply prices is just equal to the interregional transmission cost plus distribution cost, and when the optimal flow is zero, the difference is less than or equal to the sum of these two costs. Thus,

$$(1)\ \text{if}\ \bar{x}_{ijt} > 0,\ \bar{\rho}^1_{jt} - \bar{\rho}^2_{it} = f_{ijt} + c^*_{ijt} \tag{6.20}$$

and

$$(2)\ \text{if}\ \bar{x}_{ijt} = 0,\ \bar{\rho}^1_{jt} - \bar{\rho}^2_{it} \leq f_{ijt} + c^*_{ijt}$$

Condition (6.13) states that when there is a positive amount of electrical energy generated from plant type Θ, the discounted market supply price $\sigma^{t-1}\bar{\rho}^2_{jt}$ is equal to the discounted marginal operating cost $\sigma^{t-1}\Psi^\Theta_{jt}$ plus the discounted cost of additional capacity (investment cost) $\sigma^{t-1}\bar{\rho}^\Theta_{jt}$ for each sector, region, and time period. When there is no electrical energy generated by plant type Θ, the discounted supply price is either less than or just equal to the discounted investment cost of electrical energy generation plus the discounted marginal operating cost. In other words, when there is a positive amount of electrical energy generated from a given plant type, the market supply price for a particular region and time period will equal the operating plus investment costs, and when there is no electrical energy generated from a given plant type, the supply price is either less than or equal to the two cost components. Thus,

$$(1)\ \bar{x}^\Theta_{jt} > 0,\ \bar{\rho}^2_{jt} = \bar{\rho}^\Theta_{jt} + \Psi^\Theta_{jt} \tag{6.21}$$

and

$$(2)\ \bar{x}^\Theta_{jt} = 0,\ \bar{\rho}^2_{jt} \leq \bar{\rho}^\Theta_{jt} + \Psi^\Theta_{jt}$$

Condition (6.14) states that when there is a positive addition to generating capacity of plant type Θ, the discounted cost of additions to capacity $\sigma^{t-1}\bar{\rho}^\Theta_{jt}$, is equal to the discounted marginal cost of new plant, $\sigma^{t-1}\xi_{jt}{}^\Theta$, plus the discounted penalty society incurs for not being able to expand capacity beyond a limit imposed on it by physical, institutional, and technological limitations. When $\bar{W}^\Theta_{jt} = 0$, the discounted cost of additions to capacity is less than or equal to this latter amount. Alternatively, when there is a positive addition to generating capacity of a given plant type, the cost of capacity additions equals the marginal cost of new plant plus the penalty due to the capacity constraint on that given plant type in a given region.

When there is no addition to capacity for that given plant type, the cost of capacity additions is less than or equal to this latter amount. Thus,

$$(1) \text{ if } \overline{W}^{\theta}_{jt} > 0,\ \overline{\rho}^{\theta}_{jt} = \xi^{\theta}_{jt} + \overline{\rho}^{\theta *}_{jt} \tag{6.22}$$

$$(2) \text{ if } \overline{W}^{\theta}_{jt} = 0,\ \overline{\rho}^{\theta}_{jt} \leq \xi^{\theta}_{jt} + \overline{\rho}^{\theta *}_{jt}$$

The value of $\rho^{\theta *}_{jt}$ is interpreted as the penalty society incurs for not being able to expand capacity for a particular plant type beyond a certain limit. This term might alternately be interpreted as the marginal value of a particular plant type at time t or the amount by which a unit increment in a particular plant type at time t would increase the maximum value of net social payoff. For the considerations here though, the first interpretation is selected.

Conditions (6.15) through (6.18) are expressions of the efficient valuation of electrical energy in the economy and state that when discounted demand price, say $\sigma^{t-1}\overline{\rho}^{1}_{jt}$, and the discounted market supply price, say $\sigma^{t-1}\overline{\rho}^{2}_{jt}$, or the market demand price $\overline{\rho}^{1}_{jt}$ and market supply price $\overline{\rho}^{2}_{jt}$ are both positive then (6.3) and (6.5) hold with equality; i.e.,

$$\sum_i \overline{y}_{ijt} - \sum_i \overline{x}_{ijt} = 0,$$

$$\sum_i \overline{x}_{jit} - \sum_{\theta} \overline{x}^{\theta}_{jt} = 0;$$

and when $\sigma^{t-1}\rho^{1}_{jt} = 0$ and $\sigma^{t-1}\rho^{2}_{jt} = 0$ or $\rho^{1}_{jt} = 0$ and $\rho^{2}_{jt} = 0$, (6.3) and (6.5) may hold with either inequality or equality for each region and in each time period.

The derived conditions exactly satisfy conditions for an intertemporal-spatial equilibrium stipulated earlier in this chapter.

The Free Trade Solution

Using the information and estimates from the first five chapters, the saddle value problem can be solved in the case where interregional flows are allowed. The value of N (regions) is nine, the value of M (consuming sectors) is three, the value of T (time periods) is five, and the value of L (plant types) is three.

Before presenting the results, two potential points of confusion should be cleared away. First, the discount factor and the depreciation factor are computed on an annual basis and then aggregated to five year levels. It is these five year aggregates that are the operative factors. Second, since the optimality conditions reveal that the social rate of discount is equally distributed across all terms in each of the relations (6.11) through (6.18), the model can be solved with or without the explicit inclusion of the factor. The optimal solution, $\overline{\chi}_{ijt} = (\overline{y}_{ijt}, \overline{x}_{ijt}, \overline{x}^{\theta}_{jt}, \overline{W}^{\theta}_{jt})$, will be unaffected either way. Care must be exercised in interpreting the values of the dual variables. With the social rate of discount included, the resulting values of the dual variables are interpreted as the present value of these future prices or penalties. Without the inclusion of the factor, the resulting values are just the current period values. Note that by omitting the social rate of discount in computing the optimal solution, one can nicely skirt the problem of the choice of an appropriate rate of social discount. This is the course selected here. If one feels uncomfortable with this approach, it is a simple matter to discount the values of the dual variables that are obtained by whatever value desired.

In the problem under investigation, a policy is sought that will insure that social welfare (net social payoff) in relation to the available electrical energy supply is maximized. Economic theory indicates that such a situation is approached when a competitive market prevails. Under these circumstances, the market price of electrical energy should be equal to the marginal cost of supplying electrical energy to the market, which in turn is equal to the value in use of the last unit of electrical energy purchased by various consumers. This is precisely what the optimality conditions given above, if they hold with equality, guarantee.[13] Marglin has evaluated the acceptability of the use of this approach in relation to water resource development and found the assumptions underlying the concept of net social payoff not unduly restrictive.[14] His comments carry over to the current discussion.

One point that might be overlooked needs some clarification. The supply curve for each plant type for each of the time periods and for each of the regions is horizontal up to the capacity limitations imposed by existing plant and maximum new capacity additions. At this point it becomes vertical. Hence, the optimal price resulting from the competitive model might be greater than short-run cost and investment cost since the consumer might pay a penalty because society is not able to expand indefinitely capacity of a given plant type.

Assuming that a competitive market prevails across all producing and consuming sectors, all regions, and all time periods and using the data that has previously been presented, the solution to the saddle value problem can be found in tables 6-1 through 6-9. Not all of the values are given since some of them can be obtained simply by combining previous information with the optimal demand prices. Specifically, the quantities demanded can be obtained by inserting the prices into the demand equations given in Table 3-4 through Table 3-6 and solving for $\overline{y}_{ijt}$. To obtain the optimal supply price, simply subtract the distribution cost given in Chapter 4 (page 45) from the corresponding demand price. The $\overline{\rho}^{\theta}_{jt}$ is the supply price minus the short-

Table 6-1
Optimal Flows of Electrical Energy Generated in 1970 by Region
(kWh in Billions)
(Values when Trade Prohibited in Parentheses)

From To	*NE*[a]	*MA*	*ENC*	*WNC*	*SA*	*ESC*	*WSC*	*M*	*P*
1. NE	53.70 (53.70)								
2. MA	1.26 (0.0)	187.78 (189.04)							
3. ENC			256.99 (256.99)						
4. WNC				87.45 (87.45)					
5. SA					209.75 (209.75)				
6. ESC	0.01 (0.0)			1.67 (0.0)	3.59 (0.0)	129.18 (134.55)			
7. WSC				0.09 (0.0)			146.49 (147.38)		
8. M								59.63 (59.63)	
9. P									194.57 (194.57)

[a]The regional abbreviations denote thc New England region, the Middle Atlantic region, and so on.

Table 6-2
Optimal Flows of Electrical Energy Generated in 1975 by Region
(kWh in Billions)
(Values when Trade Prohibited in Parentheses)

From To	*NE*	*MA*	*ENC*	*WNC*	*SA*	*ESC*	*WSC*	*M*	*P*
1. NE	84.23 (85.39)	6.55 (0.0)							
2. MA		248.02 (248.02)							
3. ENC			310.12 (310.12)						
4. WNC			28.58 (0.0)	131.25 (131.25)					
5. SA					262.01 (262.01)				
6. ESC					40.19 (0.0)	172.26 (174.82)			
7. WSC							219.19 (219.19)		
8. M								75.06 (75.06)	
9. P									251.74 (251.74)

Table 6-3
Optimal Flows of Electrical Energy Generated in 1980 by Region
(kWh in Billions)
(Values when Trade Prohibited in Parentheses)

From To	*NE*	*MA*	*ENC*	*WNC*	*SA*	*ESC*	*WSC*	*M*	*P*
1. NE	94.29 (94.29)								
2. MA		282.24 (282.24)							
3. ENC			361.04 (361.04)						
4. WNC			17.09 (0.0)	148.63 148.63)					
5. SA					317.15 (317.15)				
6. ESC					28.36 (0.0)	202.03 (202.03)			
7. WSC							245.17 (245.17)		
8. M								83.02 (83.02)	
9. P									274.01 (274.01)

Table 6-4
Optimal Flows of Electrical Energy Generated in 1985 by Region
(kWh in Billions)
(Values when Trade Prohibited in Parentheses)

From *To*	*NE*	*MA*	*ENC*	*WNC*	*SA*	*ESC*	*WSC*	*M*	*P*
1. NE	109.79 (109.79)								
2. MA		327.34 (327.34)							
3. ENC			449.77 (449.77)						
4. WNC				175.17 (175.17)					
5. SA					385.60 (385.60)				
6. ESC					25.35 (0.0)	242^{x} 0 (242.10)			
7. WSC							295.47 (295.47)		
8. M								95.39 (95.39)	
9. P									320.91 (320.91)

Table 6-5
Optimal Flows of Electrical Energy Generated in 1990 by Region
(kWh in Billions)
(Values when Trade Prohibited in Parentheses)

From To	*NE*	*MA*	*ENC*	*WNC*	*SA*	*ESC*	*WSC*	*M*	*P*
1. NE	130.12 (130.12)								
2. MA		385.26 (385.26)							
3. ENC			522.26 (522.26)						
4. WNC				210.31 (210.31)					
5. SA					494.24 (494.24)				
6. ESC						283.98 (283.98)			
7. WSC							348.33 (348.33)		
8. M								110.78 (110.78)	
9. P									375.06 (375.06)

Table 6-6
Optimal Generation by Plant Type by Region for Each Year
(kWh in Billions)
(Values when Trade Prohibited in Parentheses)

Region	*Year*	*Hydroelectric Plants*	*Fossil-fueled Plants*	*Nuclear Plants*
1. New England	1970	4.17	45.27	4.27
		(4.17)	(45.27)	(4.27)
	1975	6.35	41.67	42.76
		(6.35)	(36.28)	(42.76)
	1980	8.54	36.03	49.72
		(8.54)	(33.85)	(51.91)
	1985	11.14	31.15	67.50
		(11.14)	(29.27)	(69.38)
	1990	13.75	26.94	89.44
		(13.75)	(25.31)	(91.07)
2. Middle Atlantic	1970	22.83	158.91	7.30
		(22.83)	(158.91)	(7.30)
	1975	36.80	146.37	64.85
		(36.80)	(146.37)	(64.85)
	1980	50.76	126.57	104.91
		(50.76)	(126.57)	(104.91)
	1985	67.34	109.45	150.56
		(67.34)	(109.45)	(150.56)
	1990	83.90	94.64	206.72
		(83.90)	(94.64)	(206.72)
3. East North Central	1970	3.40	250.88	2.71
		(3.40)	(250.88)	(2.71)
	1975	10.96	264.19	34.97
		(10.96)	(264.19)	(34.97)
	1980	18.52	275.70	66.82
		(18.52)	(275.70)	(66.82)
	1985	35.49	263.38	150.90
		(35.49)	(363.31)	(150.90)
	1990	52.46	233.31	236.49
		(52.46)	(233.31)	(236.49)
4. West North Central	1970	12.09	75.36	0.0
		(12.09)	(75.36)	(0.0)
	1975	13.36	93.91	52.56
		(13.36)	(65.33)	(52.56)
	1980	14.64	81.21	69.87
		(14.64)	(56.49)	(77.50)
	1985	17.09	70.22	87.86
		(17.09)	(48.85)	(109.22)
	1990	19.55	60.72	130.04
		(19.55)	(42.24)	(148.52)
5. South Atlantic	1970	10.55	199.20	0.0
		(10.55)	(199.20)	(0.0)
	1975	14.68	201.34	45.99
		(14.68)	(201.34)	(45.99)
	1980	18.81	203.18	95.16
		(18.81)	(203.08)	(95.16)

Table 6-6 (continued)
Optimal Generation by Plant Type by Region for Each Year
(kWh in Billions)
(Values when Trade Prohibited in Parentheses)

Region	*Year*	*Hydroelectric Plants*	*Fossil-fueled Plants*	*Nuclear Plants*
	1985	24.62	233.86	127.12
		(24.62)	(233.86)	(127.12)
	1990	32.68	283.12	178.44
		(32.68)	(283.12)	(178.44)
6. East South Central	1970	17.32	117.23	0.0
		(17.32)	(117.23)	(0.0)
	1975	23.29	130.03	59.13
		(23.29)	(92.40)	(59.13)
	1980	29.25	82.54	118.60
		(29.25)	(54.17)	(118.60)
	1985	40.81	97.23	129.41
		(40.81)	(75.80)	(125.48)
	1990	52.36	84.07	147.54
		(52.36)	(65.54)	(166.07)
7. West South Central	1970	3.86	143.52	0.0
		(3.86)	(143.52)	(0.0)
	1975	8.67	177.66	32.85
		(8.67)	(177.66)	(32.85)
	1980	13.49	166.52	65.16
		(13.49)	(166.52)	(65.16)
	1985	20.22	143.99	131.25
		(20.22)	(143.99)	(131.25)
	1990	18.75	124.51	205.06
		(18.75)	(124.51)	(205.06)
8. Mountain	1970	22.19	37.44	0.0
		(22.19)	(37.44)	(0.0)
	1975	27.95	40.54	6.57
		(27.95)	(40.54)	(6.57)
	1980	33.70	35.06	14.26
		(33.70)	(35.06)	(14.26)
	1985	39.75	30.31	25.33
		(39.75)	(30.31)	(25.33)
	1990	45.79	26.21	38.78
		(45.79)	(26.21)	(38.78)
9. Pacific	1970	116.87	72.82	4.88
		(116.87)	(72.82)	(4.88)
	1975	145.88	48.86	57.01
		(145.88)	(48.86)	(57.01)
	1980	174.90	54.45	44.66
		(174.90)	(54.45)	(44.66)
	1985	205.41	47.08	68.42
		(205.41)	(47.08)	(68.42)
	1990	235.94	40.71	98.41
		(235.94)	(40.71)	(98.41)

Table 6-7
Optimal Investment in New Generating Capacity by Plant Type for Each Year by Region
(kWh in Billions)
(Values when Trade Prohibited in Parentheses)

Region	*Year*	*Hydroelectric Plants*	*Fossil-fueled Plants*	*Nuclear Plants*
1. New England	1975	2.49	2.52	39.42
		(2.49)	(0.0)	(39.42)
	1980	2.65	0.0	16.22
		(2.65)	(0.0)	(18.40)
	1985	3.22	0.0	28.54
		(3.22)	(0.0)	(28.71)
	1990	3.41	0.0	36.55)
		(3.41)	(0.0)	(36.71)
2. Middle Atlantic	1975	15.64	8.96	59.13
		(15.64)	(8.96)	(59.13)
	1980	16.63	0.0	54.10
		(16.63)	(0.0)	(54.10)
	1985	20.27	0.0	68.36
		(20.27)	(0.0)	(68.36)
	1990	21.46	0.0	88.75
		(21.46)	(0.0)	(88.75)
3. East North Central	1975	7.81	47.25	32.85
		(7.81)	(47.25)	(32.85)
	1980	8.35	47.25	39.42
		(8.35)	(47.25)	(39.42)
	1985	18.31	24.98	98.55
		(18.31)	(24.98)	(98.55)
	1990	19.55	5.56	118.26
		(19.55)	(5.56)	(111.26)
4. West North Central	1975	2.15	28.75	52.56
		(2.15)	(0.17)	(52.56)
	1980	2.25	0.0	28.69
		(2.25)	(0.0)	(36.32)
	1985	3.51	0.0	33.11
		(3.51)	(0.0)	(48.51)
	1990	3.70	0.0	61.20
		(3.70)	(0.0)	(62.94)
5. South Atlantic	1975	4.90	29.08	45.99
		(4.90)	(29.08)	(45.99)
	1980	5.19	29.08	59.13
		(5.19)	(29.08)	(59.13)
	1985	7.18	58.16	52.56
		(7.18)	(58.16)	(52.56)
	1990	9.84	80.90	78.84
		(9.84)	(80.90)	(78.84)
6. East South Central	1975	7.23	28.66	59.13
		(7.23)	(0.0)	(59.13)
	1980	7.66	0.0	72.27
		(7.66)	(0.0)	(72.27)

Table 6-7 (continued)
Optimal Investment in New Generating Capacity by Plant Type for Each Year by Reqion
(kWh in Billions)
(Values when Trade Prohibited in Parentheses)

Region	*Year*	*Hydroelectric Plants*	*Fossil-fueled Plants*	*Nuclear Plants*
	1985	13.68	0.0	36.48
		(13.68)	(0.0)	(32.56)
	1990	14.52	0.0	46.14
		(14.52)	(0.0)	(67.75)
7. West South Central	1975	5.09	53.56	32.85
		(5.09)	(53.56)	(32.85)
	1980	5.44	12.90	39.42
		(5.44)	(12.90)	(39.42)
	1985	7.72	0.0	80.20
		(7.72)	(0.0)	(80.20)
	1990	0.0	0.0	102.22
		(0.0)	(0.0)	(102.22)
8. Mountain	1975	7.37	8.17	6.57
		(7.37)	(8.17)	(6.57)
	1980	7.79	0.0	9.11
		(7.79)	(0.0)	(9.11)
	1985	8.49	0.0	14.16
		(8.49)	(0.0)	(14.16)
	1990	8.93	0.0	18.93
		(8.93)	(0.0)	(18.93)
9. Pacific	1975	37.49	0.0	53.18
		(37.49)	(0.0)	(53.18)
	1980	39.63	0.0	0.0
		(39.63)	(0.0)	(0.0)
	1985	43.21	0.0	33.43
		(43.21)	(0.0)	(33.43)
	1990	45.45	0.0	44.80
		(45.45)	(0.0)	(44.80)

run marginal cost given, of course, that the corresponding x_{jt}^{0} is positive. Otherwise the value is zero.

The total value of the undiscounted net social payoff (NSP) is equal to \$470,551.96. There are significant interregional transmissions of electrical energy that would have been desirable from the net social payoff maximization criterion in 1970 and that would be desirable in 1975, 1980, and 1985. The quantity of the interregional flow falls to zero by 1990.

Focusing on the year 1970 in Table 6-9, it is interesting to observe the penalty society has incurred for having an insufficient supply of generating capacity at the prevailing price. This penalty ranges as high as 22.5 mills and as low as 3.91 mills. This says that if generating capacity had been

Table 6-8
Optimal Demand Price by Region for Each Year
(Mills per kWh)
(Price when Trade Prohibited in Parentheses)

Region	*1970*	*1975*	*1980*	*1985*	*1990*
1. New England	18.82	9.29	7.95	7.74	10.80
	(20.08)	(8.30)	(7.95)	(7.74)	(10.80)
2. Middle Atlantic	17.94	10.17	8.00	7.79	11.12
	(17.63)	(11.81)	(8.00)	(7.79)	(11.12)
3. East North Central	15.88	11.69	10.01	7.94	11.16
	(15.88)	(16.40)	(12.86)	(7.94)	(11.16)
4. West North Central	16.87	9.64	7.95	7.75	10.81
	(18.24)	(9.64)	(7.95)	(7.75)	(10.81)
5. South Atlantic	14.58	9.69	8.53	8.29	10.78
	(15.30)	(17.09)	(13.68)	(12.40)	(10.78)
6. East South Central	13.95	9.06	7.89	7.66	10.35
	(11.80)	(8.30)	(7.89)	(7.66)	(10.35)
7. West South Central	14.84	8.62	9.01	7.68	10.45
	(14.59)	(8.62)	(9.01)	(7.68)	(10.45)
8. Mountain	15.06	10.44	7.92	7.69	10.53
	(15.06)	(10.44)	(7.92)	(7.69)	(10.53)
9. Pacific	14.78	8.30	7.94	7.76	10.92
	(14.78)	(8.30)	(7.94)	(7.76)	(10.92)

expanded by one kWh, net social payoff would have increased between 3.91 and 22.5 mills depending on the plant type and region in which the expansion occurred. Of course the development of generating capacity, as has been previously discussed, depends on a large number of factors, any of which limit the expansion of existing capacity. Nevertheless, it is interesting to see what benefit would accrue to society if additional capacity had been available. If expected additions to new capacity materialize, this penalty will fall dramatically towards zero for fossil and nuclear plants and becomes increasingly smaller for hydroelectric plants, given they are the least expensive way of generating electrical energy, unless the demand for electrical energy were limited to the extent that hydroelectric generation could supply all of the electrical energy demanded. It also indicates that a concerted effort be made in expanding hydroelectric sites beyond the physical and technological limitations existing as long as the operation and maintenance cost and capital cost do not exceed those of the other plant types. If it is true that only 30 percent of the total potential capacity of hydroelectric plants has been developed,[15] it might serve society well to invest in the research and development efforts required to expand hydroelectric capacity beyond the anticipated limitations. Alternately, geothermal plants, an insignificant factor in the present and projected generation of electrical energy, might more seriously be considered as a viable alternative to the generation of electrical energy since their operation and maintenance and capital costs are expected to be the same as those for hydroelectric plants.[16]

The optimal quantities demanded by each sector for each of the regions changes from the actual amount consumed in 1970 as one would expect given that a uniform price is charged to each of the consuming sectors in 1970. The optimal quantity demanded by the residential sector increases about 5 percent in each of the regions over the actual 1970 value and the optimal quantity demanded by the commercial sector increases by about 15 percent. For the industrial sector, the optimal quantity demanded falls about 14 percent from the actual 1970 value. Thus, in 1970 not only were the residential and commercial sectors on the average charged too high a price for the electrical energy they consumed, they also were allocated less than the amount the societal optimum would dictate.

The marginal cost pricing concept is at work in the model to determine the optimal pricing scheme.[17] For the plant type where the additions to capacity constraint is not binding, the optimal price is determined to be the short-run marginal cost of operation plus the marginal cost of adding a unit of this capacity to active operation plus the distribution cost (assuming there are no interregional flows). Thus, for example, in the Pacific region in 1990, the optimal price of electrical energy is 10.92 mills per kWh, of which 4.92 mills is for distribution cost, 0.68, 2.43, and 1.93 mills are for short-run marginal costs for hydroelectric, fossil, and nuclear generation, respectively, and 2.29 and 4.07 mills are the marginal costs for adding new capacity for hydroelectric and nuclear plants. (No fossil plants are to be added in this period). A penalty of 3.02 mills per kWh is incurred because of the limitation on the expansion of hydroelectric generating capacity.

Summarily, when capacity is fully utilized, the full marginal cost of capacity consisting of the short-run marginal cost, distribution cost, and investment cost plus any interregional transmission cost, if electrical energy is transmitted into the region, is charged. In an off-peak period when no new capacity needs to be added, the charge would be limited to the marginal cost of operation, the distribution cost, plus any interregional transmission cost, if it is incurred. This latter statement is implicit when one observes that before any new capacity is added, the existing generating capacity is utilized to its fullest extent.

The overall price profile that results is a most revealing aspect of the model. If one truly believes that the electrical energy industry should be regulated in such a way as to approximate the competitive norm, then the regulatory commissions are sadly remiss in setting the rate structure. As was noted above, not only should a uniform price be charged to each sector for the homogeneous good, which currently is not the practice, but this

Table 6-9
Shadow Prices on Capacity Expansion
(Mills per kWh)
(Values when Trade Prohibited in Parentheses)

Region	*Year*	*Hydroelectric Plants*	*Fossil-fueled Plants*	*Nuclear Plants*
1. New England	1970	20.59	9.10	10.38
		(20.93)	(9.50)	(10.86)
	1975	8.69	0.0	1.03
		(7.69)	(0.0)	(1.04)
	1980	5.87	0.0	0.0
		(5.87)	(0.0)	(0.0)
	1985	4.03	0.0	0.0
		(4.08)	(0.0)	(0.0)
	1990	2.20	0.0	0.0
		(2.20)	(0.0)	(0.0)
2. Middle Atlantic	1970	21.25	8.80	10.11
		(22.45)	(9.90)	(11.08)
	1975	10.34	0.72	1.87
		(11.97)	(2.30)	(3.50)
	1980	6.68	0.0	0.0
		(6.68)	(0.0)	(0.0)
	1985	4.84	0.0	0.0
		(4.84)	(0.0)	(0.0)
	1990	3.00	0.0	0.0
		(3.00)	(0.0)	(0.0)
3. East North Central	1970	22.50	10.18	10.84
		(29.32)	(16.38)	(16.27)
	1975	13.90	4.64	5.36
		(21.25)	(11.80)	(12.30)
	1980	8.89	1.79	2.45
		(11.74)	(4.64)	(5.30)
	1985	5.06	0.0	0.49
		(5.06)	(0.0)	(0.49)
	1990	3.07	0.0	0.37
		(3.07)	(0.0)	(0.37)
4. West North Central	1970	18.59	7.12	8.71
		(19.97)	(8.49)	(10.09)
	1975	8.65	0.0	1.37
		(8.65)	(0.0)	(0.0)
	1980	5.47	0.0	0.0
		(5.47)	(0.0)	(0.0)
	1985	3.61	0.0	0.0
		(3.61)	(0.0)	(0.0)
	1990	1.76	0.0	0.0
		(1.76)	(0.0)	(0.0)
5. South Atlantic	1970	17.07	6.35	7.31
		(32.35)	(19.97)	(18.96)
	1975	9.48	1.67	2.46
		(25.19)	(16.60)	(16.42)
	1980	6.32	0.65	1.26
		(15.28)	(9.36)	(9.63)

Table 6-9 (continued)
Shadow Prices on Capacity Expansion
(Mills per kWh)
(Values when Trade Prohibited in Parentheses)

Region	Year	*Hydroelectric Plants*	*Fossil-fueled Plants*	*Nuclear Plants*
	1985	3.92	0.37	0.81
		(8.02)	(4.48)	(4.92)
	1990	1.51	0.0	0.27
		(1.51)	(0.0)	(0.27)
6. East South Central	1970	15.46	4.28	5.47
		(12.60)	(1.48)	(2.73)
	1975	8.38	0.0	0.88
		(7.62)	(0.0)	(0.12)
	1980	5.79	0.0	0.01
		(5.79)	(0.0)	(0.01)
	1985	3.99	0.0	0.0
		(3.99)	(0.0)	(0.0)
	1990	2.23	0.0	0.0
		(2.23)	(0.0)	(0.0)
7. West South Central	1970	14.92	5.13	6.66
		(14.66)	(4.87)	(6.40)
	1975	6.91	0.0	1.29
		(6.91)	(0.0)	(1.29)
	1980	4.74	0.0	1.12
		(4.74)	(0.0)	(1.12)
	1985	1.73	0.0	0.0
		(1.73)	(0.0)	(0.0)
	1990	0.0	0.0	0.0
		(0.0)	(0.0)	(0.0)
8. Mountain	1970	17.87	5.94	7.60
		(17.87)	(5.94)	(7.60)
	1975	9.79	0.71	2.23
		(9.79)	(0.71)	(2.23)
	1980	5.82	0.0	0.0
		(5.82)	(0.0)	(0.0)
	1985	4.02	0.0	0.0
		(4.02)	(0.0)	(0.0)
	1990	2.23	0.0	0.0
		(2.23)	(0.0)	(0.0)
9. Pacific	1970	16.31	3.91	5.53
		(16.31)	(3.91)	(5.53)
	1975	8.40	0.0	0.0
		(8.40)	(0.0)	(5.53)
	1980	6.62	0.0	0.0
		(6.62)	(0.0)	(0.0)
	1985	4.83	0.0	0.0
		(4.83)	(0.0)	(0.0)
	1990	3.02	0.0	0.0
		(3.02)	(0.0)	(0.0)

price, rather than following the expected increase, should fall until 1985, at which point it should increase slightly. Ignoring the price differentials among sectors in a given region, the average price paid for electrical energy in 1970, given the existing capacity constraints, is in the neighborhood of 5 to 10 percent too high, using the optimal demand price of Table 6-8 as the base. This inefficiency will continue in subsequent periods and become more pronounced if the projected trend in prices (see chapter 3) obtain. Using average prices again across a region, the price that is expected to be charged will be in the range of 2 to 3 times greater than what the competitive solution suggests is optimal. This statement is conditional on all of the assumptions that have been made heretofore. Such things as the expected growth of demand, the limitations on additions to capacity of a particular plant type, the correct estimation of future short-run and long-run marginal costs, and so on all effect the optimal price. Nevertheless, even with a wide margin for error in these assumptions, unless the regulatory commissions take a careful look at the costs involved when revising the rate schedules that utilities are allowed to apply, there will be gross inefficiencies in the pricing and consequently the allocation of electrical energy. The inefficiency in the allocation will not be quite as exaggerated as that found for many durable commodities though, where price discrimination is practiced, because of the relative price inelasticity of demand for electrical energy.

As has been frequently observed in the foregoing pages, costs are the most significant consideration in the economic analysis of determining the least-cost investment in electrical energy generation. Investment decisions to be made in any period depend upon the past and future evolution of factor prices. This was made abundantly clear when the values for the short-run marginal cost and the cost of new capacity were obtained. The optimality conditions of equations (6.11) through (6.18) indicate that when investment is made in new capacity, investment in the plant type with the lowest combined operation and maintenance cost and investment cost is undertaken first up to the permissible limit and then investment in the plant type with the second lowest combined costs is undertaken, imposing a penalty on society because capacity of the first plant type is limited. This investment selection process is repeated until consumers are supplied with the amount of electrical energy for which they are willing to pay.

Note that with only a few exceptions across all time periods and regions, hydroelectric additions are undertaken first, with nuclear plants second. The fossil-fueled additions to capacity make up the residual supply, falling to zero in some regions in the later periods. In the first period in which investment is permitted (i.e., 1975), the additions to capacity for each plant type in almost all regions are undertaken to the maximum limit. However, as the year 1990 is approached, investment activity falls away from the limit in almost all instances except for hydroelectric plants. In fact in 1990, the optimal solution indicates that minimal investment in fossil-fueled plants should occur. If this is the pattern that develops, the electrical energy industry must continually revise its investment plans and limit actual investment in new nuclear and fossil-fueled generating facilities accordingly.

A Restriction on Free Trade: The Case of No Interregional Flows

Presently it is remarkable how little electrical energy appears to move between states and between regions.[18] With the expansion of the extra-high voltage lines, increased interconnection of power systems makes it feasible to exchange electrical energy over long distances. Unfortunately, this is not yet a normal part of the electrical energy picture.[19]

It will be argued in what follows that this lack of interregional transmission (or trade) of electrical energy has the effect of reducing social welfare. It has been long recognized that some trade is always at least potentially beneficial.[20] If one regards the United States as the group whose welfare it is desired to maximize, and if conditions favorable for the achievement of an optimum exist, free trade will be optimal in the sense that it leads to the nation's welfare frontier.[21] However, if one is interested in maximizing the welfare of a particular region rather than that of the whole nation, one would prefer movement along the frontier in a direction which favors the region with whom the concern rests. This can be done by the restriction of flows to and from the region.

The idea that free trade of electrical energy maximizes national welfare presupposes optimum conditions of production and allocation within all regions and full employment. To the person who criticizes this supposition, the response is that production and allocation conditions within regions may be taken as data; and trade takes place on the basis of comparative prices and not comparative costs. Free trade, if anything, tends to decrease degrees of monopoly within regions and it may effect an improvement even if it cannot be held to maximize national welfare. It should be conceded that the idea of free trade does ignore the distribution of income between regions. This problem is not discussed here.[22]

What can one say quantitatively then about the cost to society of the present policy of restricting interregional flows of electrical energy supposing the electrical energy industry were to operate in a perfectly competitive environment? The answer to this question can be found in the results of the model presented in Tables 6-1 through 6-10. The prohibition of interreg-

Table 6-10
Shadow Prices on Interregional Flow Restrictions
(Mills per kWh)

Region From	*Region To*	*Year*	*Shadow Price*
MA	NE	1970	1.57
ENC	NE	1970	0.12
ENC	WNC	1970	0.30
SA	NE	1970	0.38
ESC	NE	1970	3.41
ESC	MA	1970	1.82
ESC	ENC	1970	1.41
ESC	WNC	1970	3.52
ESC	SA	1970	2.86
ESC	WSC	1970	0.06
WSC	WNC	1970	1.63
M	WNC	1970	0.71
NE	MA	1975	2.63
NE	ENC	1975	4.03
NE	SA	1975	4.39
MA	ENC	1975	1.15
MA	SA	1975	1.74
WNC	ENC	1975	4.70
WNC	SA	1975	4.15
ESC	ENC	1975	5.43
ESC	SA	1975	8.16
WSC	ENC	1975	3.93
WSC	SA	1975	5.10
M	ENC	1975	1.81
M	SA	1975	0.86
NE	ENC	1980	0.84
NE	SA	1980	1.33
MA	ENC	1960	1.42
MA	SA	1980	2.15
WNC	ENC	1980	2.85
WNC	SA	1980	2.42
ESC	ENC	1980	2.30
ESC	SA	1980	5.16
WSC	ENC	1980	0.01
WSC	SA	1980	1.30
M	ENC	1980	0.80
NE	SA	1985	0.25
MA	SA	1985	1.07
ENC	SA	1985	1.47
WNC	SA	1985	1.35
ESC	SA	1985	4.10
WSC	SA	1985	1.35

ional flows is accomplished by the imposition of the constraint $x_{ijt} \leq 0$ for all $i \neq j$ and for all i, j, and t.

With the adoption of this additional constraint, the saddle value problem of equation (6.10) is altered by the addition of the term $\sum \sigma^{t-1} \sum_j \sum_{i \neq j} \bar{\rho}^3_{ijt} (0 - x_{ijt})$ so that the problem is to find a saddle point of the Lagrangian

$$\Phi^* (\chi,\rho^*) = \Phi (\chi,\rho) + \sum_t \sigma^{t-1} \sum_j \sum_{i \neq j} \rho^3_{ijt} (0 - x_{ijt}). \qquad (6.10a)$$

This has the effect of changing optimality condition (6.12) to the following:

$$\frac{\partial \overline{\Phi}^*}{\partial x_{ijt}} = -\sigma^{t-1} f_{ijt} - \sigma^{t-1} c^*_{ijt} + \sigma^{t-1} \bar{\rho}^1_{jt} - \sigma^{t-1} \bar{\rho}^2_{it} - \sigma^{t-1} \bar{\rho}^3_{ijt} \leq 0 \qquad (6.12a)$$

or simply

$$-f_{ijt} - c^*_{ijt} + \bar{\rho}^1_{jt} - \bar{\rho}^2_{it} - \bar{\rho}^3_{ijt} \leq 0$$

and

$$\frac{\partial \overline{\Phi}^*}{\partial x_{ijt}} \bar{x}_{ijt} = 0, \text{ for all } i, j, \text{ and } t.$$

Condition (6.12a) states that when the optimal flow $\bar{x}_{ijt}$ is positive, the difference between the discounted market demand and discounted market supply prices is equal to the discounted interregional transmission cost plus distribution cost plus a penalty for not allowing interregional flows. If $\bar{x}_{ijt} = 0$, the difference is less than or equal to the sum of these values. Stated differently, when the optimal flow is positive, the difference between the market demand and market supply prices is just equal to interregional transmission and distribution cost plus a penalty (which might be zero), and when the optimal flow is zero the difference is less than or equal to the sum of the three terms.

Thus,

$$\text{(1) if } \bar{x}_{ijt} > 0, \quad \bar{\rho}^1_{jt} - \bar{\rho}^2_{it} = f_{ijt} + c^*_{ijt} + \bar{\rho}^3_{ijt} \qquad (6.20a)$$

and

$$\text{(2) if } \bar{x}_{ijt} = 0, \quad \bar{\rho}^1_{jt} - \bar{\rho}^2_{it} \leq f_{ijt} + c^*_{ijt} + \bar{\rho}^3_{ijt}$$

The nonzero values of the $\bar{\rho}^3_{ijt}$ are found in Table 6-10. In comparing these values to the free trade solution, one finds that for the unrestricted model interregional flows from region i to region j in time period t take place when this penalty (or shadow price) $\bar{\rho}^3_{ijt}$ in the restricted model is greater than or equal to the interregional transmission charge, f_{ijt}. In this no trade case, the f_{ijt} is zero. Transmission would have taken place had consumers been willing to pay the total transmission charge. This being true and at the same time trade being restricted, a penalty is incurred that is greater than or equal to the charge. The second half of (6.20a) says that a penalty might arise even if no interregional flow is optimal simply because the consumer, while wanting more electrical energy at the prevailing supply price within the region, is not willing to bear the entire cost of transmission from another region.

All of this is seen in Table 6-10. The penalty for interregional flow restriction is at least as large as the transmission charge between regions in the unrestricted model when trade occurred and in several more situations, a penalty due to the constraint is incurred though it does not indicate a strong enough desire on the part of the consumer in a region to have additional electrical energy.

To complete the optimality conditions for the case of no interregional flows, the following constraint must be added:

$$\frac{\partial \bar{\Phi}^*}{\partial \rho_{ijt}^3} = \sigma^{t-1} (-\bar{x}_{ijt}) \geq 0 \tag{6.26}$$

or

$$-\bar{x}_{ijt} \geq 0$$

and

$$\frac{\partial \bar{\Phi}^*}{\partial \rho_{ijt}^3} \quad \bar{\rho}_{ijt}^3 = 0, \text{ for } i \neq j \text{ and all } i, j, \text{ and } t.$$

This states that the flow of electrical energy is restricted to be less than or equal to zero when $\bar{\rho}_{ijt}^3$ is positive and that it is zero or potentially negative when $\bar{\rho}_{ijt}^3$ is zero. However, when this condition is combined with the stipulation that the values of all of the primal variables are nonnegative, the value of $\bar{x}_{ijt}$ will always be forced to equal zero for situations where $i \neq j$ and for all t.

The undiscounted value of the net social payoff when trade is prohibited is equal to \$470,160.01. Since the greatest quantity of the interregional flows of electrical energy take place in the first periods, the present value of the gain in net social payoff is understated between this and the free trade case. Had present values of net social payoff been calculated, the relative benefit to society of interregional transmission of electrical energy would have been more pronounced. As it is, the gains are slight.

Most of the effects on generation of the transmission restrictions are felt in the West North Central region and the East South Central region. This is because these regions possess lower capital cost and lower aggregate demand at a given price level than the surrounding regions. In the regions to which electrical energy would be transmitted if allowed, the demand price predictably rises due to the existence of a higher penalty arising from the capacity addition constraints or due to a higher marginal cost resulting from a larger investment in new generating capacity. Thus the East North Central region in 1980 must invest in new generating capacity to supply electrical energy that had, under free trade, been transmitted from the West North Central region. Consequently, the demand price is higher. The big jump in demand price in the East North Central region in 1975 and in the South Atlantic region in 1975, 1980, and 1985 results from paying an increased penalty arising from the limitations on additions to new generating capacity.

Everything moves predictably. Regions that have an economic advantage in the generation of electrical energy are able to supply a greater quantity of electrical energy at a lower price to their consumers. This is at the expense of other regions that are forced to charge a higher price with the resultant decrease in the quantity demanded. In the former case, regional social payoff expands, in the latter case, regional social payoff contracts. In the aggregate, society is worse off.

That the model is sensitive to demand movements is apparent from the development planning for new nuclear generating capacity. With the change in the demand structure due to the limiting of interregional transmissions, optimal investment is altered in several of the regions in the latter periods. Thus, in the West North Central region in 1985, for example, optimal investment in new nuclear generating capacity increases from 33.11 billion kWh before the restriction to 48.51 billion kWh when trade is disallowed.

An Intertemporal-Spatial Monopoly Problem

Assume that for the *M* consuming sectors, *N* regions, *L* plant types, and *T* time periods net generation of electrical energy is completely controlled by a central authority whose behavior is that of a monopolist.[23] Further assume that this central authority has generating plants in all of the *N* regions, buys its factors of production in competitive markets, and is not a monopsonist in the factor market and that the resale of electrical energy between regions is not possible. Assume that the regional demand and cost functions are the same as those described by equations (6.1a) through (6.2b).

It is important to emphasize the crucial assumption of no resale among regions, which means that arbitrager's actions in each region are completely suppressed and thus the central authority can practice price discrimination.[24] Assume that the transmission and distribution activities play passive roles in transmitting and distributing a given quantity x_{ijt} determined by the central authority from one region to another at a fixed kWh rate, $c^*_{ijt} + f_{ijt}$. Within this setting the objective of the central authority is to maximize total profits over all regions and for all time periods where the profit from sales over all of the regions for all of the time periods (appropriately discounted) is:

$$\Pi = \text{total revenue} - \text{total cost} - \text{transmission and distribution costs} \tag{6.23}$$

$$= \sum_t \sigma^{t-1} \Big[\sum_i \sum_j (\lambda_{ijt} - \omega_{ijt} y_{ijt})\, y_{ijt}$$

$$- \sum_j \sum_\Theta \Psi^\Theta_{jt}\, x^\Theta_{jt} - \sum_j \sum_\Theta \xi^\Theta_{jt} W^\Theta_{jt}$$

$$- \sum_i \sum_j f_{ijt}\, x_{ijt} - \sum_i \sum_j c^*_{ijt}\, x_{ijt} \Big]$$

It should be clear that under a pricing-allocation scheme that maximizes profits for the central authority, the market prices between regions may differ by more than the transmission cost and consequently the price system of the central authority may be quite different from that achieved under perfect competition.

As before, the demand quantities and supply quantities of electrical energy must satisfy the constraint set (6.3) through (6.7a).

In defining a monopolistic intertemporal-spatial equilibrium, the assumption of a single seller controlling the nation's market for electrical energy means that a definition of an equilibrium must be introduced that is slightly different from that found in previous sections.

As a new notation, let MR_{ijt} denote the marginal revenue from sector i in region j in period t where

$$MR_{ijt} = d(Pe_{ijt}\, y_{ijt})/dy_{ijt} = \lambda_{ijt} - 2\omega_{ijt}\, y_{ijt}$$

The marginal cost continues to be defined as before.

Given the economic environment and the marginal revenue and cost functions as they are defined here, an intertemporal-spatial monopolistic equilibrium can be defined as it was on pages 78 and following except that condition (d) will be eliminated and the following inserted in its place:

(d1) profit maximation, (by the central authority) at $(\bar{y}_{ijt}, \bar{x}_{ijt}, \bar{x}^\Theta_{jt}, \bar{W}^\Theta_{jt})$ for all $\Theta = 1, 2, \ldots, L$, $i, j = 1, 2, \ldots, N(M)$, and $t = 1, 2, \ldots, T$, where maximizing profit means maximizing equation (6.23) subject to the constraint set (6.3) through (6.7a) and $y_{ijt} \geq 0$, $x_{ijt} \geq 0$, $x^\Theta_{jt} \geq 0$, and $W^\Theta_{jt} \geq 0$.

The Lagrangian function for this monopoly problem may be written as

$$\Phi(y_{ijt}, x_{ijt}, x^\Theta_{jt}, W^\Theta_{jt}, \rho) = \sum_t \sigma^{t-1} \Big[\sum_i \sum_j (\lambda_{ijt} - \omega_{ijt}\, y_{ijt})\, y_{ijt} \tag{6.24}$$

$$
\begin{aligned}
&- \sum_j \sum_\Theta \Psi_{jt}^\Theta x_{jt}^\Theta - \sum_j \sum_\Theta \xi_{jt}^\Theta W_{jt}^\Theta \\
&- \sum_i \sum_j f_{ijt} x_{ijt} - \sum_i \sum_j c_{ijt}^* x_{ijt} \Big] \\
&+ \sum_t \sigma^{t-1} \sum_j \Big[\rho_{jt}^1 \Big(\sum_i x_{ijt} - \sum_i y_{ijt} \Big) \\
&+ \rho_{jt}^2 \Big(\sum_\Theta x_{jt}^\Theta - \sum_i x_{jit} \Big) \\
&+ \sum_\Theta \rho_{jt}^\Theta \Big(\sigma_\Theta^{t-1} S_{j1}^\Theta + \sum_{\tau=1}^{t} \sigma_\Theta^{t-\tau} W_{jt}^\Theta - x_{jt}^\Theta \Big) \\
&+ \sum_{\Theta^*} \rho_{jt}^{\Theta *} \left(\tilde{W}_{jt}^{\Theta *} - W_{jt}^{\Theta *} \right) \Big]
\end{aligned}
$$

The optimality conditions for the saddle value problem (6.24) are

$$
\frac{\partial \overline{\Phi}}{\partial y_{ijt}} = \sigma^{t-1} (\lambda_{ijt} - 2\omega_{ijt} \overline{y}_{ijt}) - \sigma^{t-1} \overline{\rho}_{jt}^1 \leq 0 \qquad (6.25)
$$

or simply

$$
\lambda_{ijt} - 2\omega_{ijt} \overline{y}_{ijt} - \overline{\rho}_{jt}^1 \leq 0
$$

and

$$
\frac{\partial \overline{\Phi}}{\partial y_{ijt}} \overline{y}_{ijt} = 0, \text{ for all } i, j, \text{ and } t
$$

with the rest of the optimality conditions identical to (6.12) through (6.18).

Now by interpreting the Lagrangians ρ_{jt}^{-1} and ρ_{jt}^{-2} as the optimum operative marginal revenue and marginal cost, the following economic interpretations can be given:

Relation (6.25) states that when discounted optimal sectoral and regional consumption for a specific time period, $\sigma^{t-1} \overline{y}_{ijt}$, is positive, the operative discounted marginal revenue to the central authority (monopolist) must be equal to the discounted marginal revenue in the ith sector and the jth region, and when $\sigma^{t-1}\overline{y}_{ijt}$ is zero, the former is greater than or equal to the latter. Stated alternately, when $\overline{y}_{ijt}$ is positive, the marginal revenue in all sectors in a region for a given time period must be equal.

The conditions identical to (6.12) through (6.18) can be given analogous interpretations to those following these equations previously. These conditions constitute the operational content of the monopolist model, and they fulfill the stipulation for an intertemporal-spatial monopolistic equilibrium provided the profit function (6.1) is a concave function.

It must be stressed that $\overline{\rho}_{jt}^1$ and $\overline{\rho}_{jt}^2$ are marginal revenues and marginal costs respectively, thus showing a striking contrast between this monopolistic case and the previous competitive case where $\bar{\rho}_{jt}^{1}$ and $\bar{\rho}_{jt}^{2}$ were market prices.

The Intertemporal-Spatial Monopoly Solution

Once again using the information and estimates from the first five chapters, the saddle value problem of equation (6.24) can be solved in the case where there is no restriction on interregional flows. There are nine regions, three consuming sectors, three plant types, and five time periods.

It is well known that monopoly will lead to a nonoptimal resource allocation. The efficiency conditions for a competitive solution will normally be violated by the monopoly market structure.[25] Note however that the only distinction necessarily implied by the pure theory of competition and monopoly is the fact that the monopolist's price exceeds marginal cost, while the price in the perfectly competitive market just equals marginal cost. It is solely on this basis that monopoly leads to an allocation of electrical energy that is inefficient.[26]

Assuming that a monopolistic market controlled by a central authority prevails across all consuming and producing sectors, all regions, and all time periods, the solution to the saddle value problem of equation (6.24) can be found in tables 6-11 through 6-19. Again, not all of the values are given since some of them can be obtained by combining previous information with the marginal revenues. The technique used to obtain quantity demanded is discussed below. Marginal cost and the ρ_{jt}^{θ} are obtained exactly as was detailed for the previous solution.

The revealing results of this solution are best looked at in comparison with the perfectly competitive solution. It is to be expected that societal welfare will be enhanced with the elimination of a central authority whose objective it is to maximize profits.[27] The magnitude of this increase can be calculated from the values of the net social payoff. The undiscounted value of *NSP* for the monopoly is equal to \$238,923.32. This says that if a central authority were allowed to operate as a monopolist in pricing and allocating electrical energy, the undiscounted societal welfare would fall by 49.2 percent over the twenty year period from the competitive net social payoff.

In just what form would total welfare decline? First note that the prices paid by each consuming sector in a region are no longer uniform. The values found in Table 6-18 are marginal revenues for the region. To obtain the price paid by a consuming sector, one would have to take the demand curve that is appropriate (found in Table 3-4, Table 3-5, or Table 3-6) and multiply the coefficients by one half. (Recall the demand curves are linear functions). Once this is done, setting the appropriate marginal revenue equal to this linear function will yield the optimal quantity demanded. Substituting this quantity demanded back into the original linear demand function will yield the price paid by the consuming sector. Thus, for the Mountain region in 1975, for example, the prices paid under monopoly conditions would be 75.60 mills, 29.10 mills, and 28.45 mills for the residential, commercial, and industrial sectors respectively.

With prices radically changing, the quantity demanded departs appreciably from the competitive solution. Using 1970 as the base, the quantity of electrical energy demanded by the residential sector on the average falls about 75 percent. For the commercial sector it falls about 40 percent, and for the industrial sector it falls about 90 percent. The monopoly price for 1970 is in the range of 50 to 80 mills for the residential sector, in the range of 20 to 35 mills for the commercial sector, and in the range of 28 to 50 mills for the industrial sector. Needless to say, electrical energy pricing and allocation in 1970 did not closely resemble the pricing and allocation one would expect to find from a monopolist who completely controls the generation and pricing of electrical energy.

Continuing to use the perfect competition model as the norm, with the drastic reduction in the quantity demanded in the monopoly situation for all sectors and over the entire time period, the amount of investment in new generating capacity is sharply curtailed. Potential hydroelectric sites for the most part continue to be fully developed and utilized. The only exceptions being in a few of the regions in 1990. Beyond that however, a limited amount of nuclear capacity and no fossil-fueled capacity is to be added. The major part of the generation of electrical energy will come from existing capacity. Note that the penalties incurred by society because of the limitations of hydroelectric plant additions to capacity are much less than they were in the case of perfect competition and are well nigh nonexistent for fossil-fueled plants and nuclear plants over the entire time period for all regions.

Summarily, by considering the foregoing monopoly model, it has been possible to look at briefly (a) the extent to which society would be harmed (measured by a decrease in the value of net social payoff) if a central authority were to act as a monopolist pricing and allocating electrical energy and (b) the price and allocation profile that would result if this central authority were allowed to exist. While it is justifiable to conclude that the electrical energy industry on the whole does not act as a spatial monopolist, one cannot conclude that monopolistic tendencies are absent from the industry. Specifically, the industry does not satisfy the efficiency conditions since it does violate and is expected to continue violating the marginal cost pricing rule.

Finally, one can look at the social welfare loss due to the restriction of interregional flows in the monopoly model as was done in the perfectly

Table 6-11
Flows of Electrical Energy Generated in 1970 by Region for the Monopoly Model
(kWh in Billions)

From To	*NE*[a]	*MA*	*ENC*	*WNC*	*SA*	*ESC*	*WSC*	*M*	*P*
1. NE	32.65								
2. MA		111.49							
3. ENC			147.47						
4. WNC				51.93					
5. SA					119.66				
6. ESC						70.27			
7. WSC							82.67		
8. M								34.05	
9. P									116.31

[a]The regional abbreviations denote the New England region, the Middle Atlantic region, and so on.

Table 6-12
Flows of Electrical Energy Generated in 1975 by Region for the Monopoly Model
(kWh in Billions)

From To	*NE*	*MA*	*ENC*	*WNC*	*SA*	*ESC*	*WSC*	*M*	*P*
1. NE	42.70								
2. MA		131.06							
3. ENC			179.68						
4. WNC				66.92					
5. SA					154.88				
6. ESC						87.41			
7. WSC							110.26		
8. M								39.11	
9. P									131.14

Table 6-13
Flows of Electrical Energy Generated in 1980 by Region for the Monopoly Model
(kWh in Billions)

From To	*NE*	*MA*	*ENC*	*WNC*	*SA*	*ESC*	*WSC*	*M*	*P*
1. NE	47.17								
2. MA		141.33							
3. ENC			195.42						
4. WNC				74.36					
5. SA					174.49				
6. ESC						101.01			
7. WSC							124.98		
8. M								41.53	
9. P									142.00

Table 6-14
Flows of Electrical Energy Generated in 1985 by Region for the Monopoly Model
(kWh in Billions)

From To	*NE*	*MA*	*ENC*	*WNC*	*SA*	*ESC*	*WSC*	*M*	*P*
1. NE	54.90								
2. MA		164.05							
3. ENC			225.55						
4. WNC				87.58					
5. SA					207.32				
6. ESC						121.16			
7. WSC							147.74		
8. M								47.76	
9. P									165.71

Table 6-15
Flows of Electrical Energy Generated in 1990 by Region for the Monopoly Model
(kWh in Billions)

From *To*	*NE*	*MA*	*ENC*	*WNC*	*SA*	*ESC*	*WSC*	*M*	*P*
1. NE	65.06								
2. MA		192.63							
3. ENC			262.56						
4. WNC				105.15					
5. SA					248.13				
6. ESC						142.53			
7. WSC							174.17		
8. M								57.79	
9. P									196.77

Table 6-16
Generation by Plant Type by Region for Each Year for the Monopoly Model
(kWh in Billions)

Region	*Year*	*Hydroelectric Plants*	*Fossil-fueled Plants*	*Nuclear Plants*
1. New England	1970	4.17	24.21	4.27
	1975	6.35	30.23	6.11
	1980	8.54	33.85	4.70
	1985	11.14	29.27	14.49
	1990	13.75	25.31	26.01
2. Middle Atlantic	1970	22.83	81.36	7.30
	1975	36.80	88.54	5.72
	1980	50.76	86.09	4.48
	1985	67.34	93.20	3.51
	1990	83.91	88.85	19.88
3. East North Central	1970	3.40	141.37	2.71
	1975	10.90	137.74	34.97
	1980	18.52	149.50	27.40
	1985	35.49	162.21	27.85
	1990	52.46	140.27	69.84
4. West North Central	1970	12.09	39.84	0.0
	1975	13.36	49.26	4.30
	1980	14.64	56.35	3.37
	1985	17.09	48.72	21.77
	1990	19.55	42.13	43.47
5. South Atlantic	1970	10.55	109.12	0.0
	1975	14.68	94.20	45.99
	1980	18.81	119.65	36.03
	1985	27.62	128.80	53.90
	1990	32.68	111.37	104.08
6. East South Central	1970	17.32	52.95	0.0
	1975	23.29	12.92	51.19
	1980	29.25	31.65	40.11
	1985	40.81	48.92	31.43
	1990	52.36	65.54	24.62
7. West South Central	1970	3.86	78.81	0.0
	1975	8.67	68.73	32.85
	1980	13.49	67.17	44.32
	1985	20.22	92.79	34.73
	1990	18.75	80.24	75.17
8. Mountain	1970	22.19	11.86	0.0
	1975	27.95	11.16	0.0
	1980	33.70	7.82	0.0
	1985	39.75	8.01	0.0
	1990	36.86	20.93	0.0
9. Pacific	1970	116.31	0.0	0.0
	1975	131.14	0.0	0.0
	1980	142.00	0.0	0.0
	1985	165.71	0.0	0.0
	1990	154.22	40.71	1.84

competitive case. However, because the monopoly solution does not yield any interregional flows, society in this instance is not penalized by the prohibition of interregional flows.

Table 6-17
Investment in New Generating Capacity by Plant Type for Each Year by Region for the Monopoly Model
(kWh in Billions)

Region	*Year*	*Hydroelectric Plants*	*Fossil-fueled Plants*	*Nuclear Plants*
1. New England	1975	2.49	0.0	2.77
	1980	2.65	0.0	0.0
	1985	3.22	0.0	10.73
	1990	3.41	0.0	14.66
2. Middle Atlantic	1975	15.64	0.0	0.0
	1980	16.63	0.0	0.0
	1985	10.27	0.0	0.0
	1990	21.46	0.0	0.0
3. East North Central	1975	7.81	0.0	32.85
	1980	8.35	0.0	0.0
	1985	18.31	0.0	6.38
	1990	19.55	0.0	48.02
4. West North Central	1975	2.15	0.0	4.30
	1980	2.25	0.0	0.0
	1985	3.51	0.0	19.13
	1990	3.70	0.0	26.42
5. South Atlantic	1975	4.90	0.0	45.99
	1980	5.19	0.0	0.0
	1985	7.18	0.0	25.66
	1990	9.84	0.0	61.85
6. East South Central	1975	7.23	0.0	51.19
	1980	7.66	0.0	0.0
	1985	13.68	0.0	0.0
	1990	14.52	0.0	0.0
7. West South Central	1975	5.09	0.0	32.85
	1980	5.44	0.0	18.59
	1985	7.72	0.0	0.0
	1990	0.0	0.0	47.96
8. Mountain	1975	7.37	0.0	0.0
	1980	7.79	0.0	0.0
	1985	8.49	0.0	0.0
	1990	0.0	0.0	0.0
9. Pacific	1975	22.76	0.0	0.0
	1980	20.39	0.0	0.0
	1985	34.03	0.0	0.0
	1990	0.5	0.0	0.0

Table 6-18
Marginal Revenue by Region for Each Year for the Monopoly Model
(Mills per kWh)

Region	*1970*	*1975*	*1980*	*1985*	*1990*
1. New England	9.41	8.30	7.90	7.75	10.80
2. Middle Atlantic	9.41	8.30	7.90	7.61	11.12
3. East North Central	9.41	8.30	7.90	7.74	10.79
4. West North Central	9.41	8.30	7.91	7.75	10.81
5. South Atlantic	9.41	8.30	7.90	7.70	10.50
6. East South Central	9.41	8.30	7.90	7.61	10.15
7. West South Central	9.41	8.30	7.90	7.68	10.45
8. Mountain	9.41	8.30	7.90	7.61	7.87
9. Pacific	6.21	6.04	5.80	5.73	7.89

Sensitivity of the Results

Throughout this study, the reasonableness of the model has been emphasized. While the model yields some interesting results, the interpretations would be misleading if the results depended on the specific data used. The estimates of costs are by no means perfectly accurate. If slight changes in estimates lead to major changes in conclusions, then the model is not at all interesting. If adjustments to demand or supply change the results appreciably, the model is of limited usefulness as a tool for policy analysis.

One could go through an elaborate procedure of changing incrementally all of the cost components to see the effects on pricing and allocation for each of the regions over the entire time period. However, in light of the optimality conditions stated on pages 81 and following, it is not necessary to go through this laborious process. By looking at the Kuhn-Tucker conditions, one can see for positive quantities of the primal variables what regional price differentials are necessary to induce interregional flows of electrical energy, for example. Or if the cost of new capacity of a given plant type were really twice the estimated value, it is apparent how this would alter the optimal demand price.

The one estimate crucial to the empirical implementation of the model, whose influence on the model's results is not immediately clear, is the estimate of the price elasticity of demand. Consequently, two additional solutions for the perfectly competitive model were obtained: one where it is assumed that the elasticity in each of the sectors is in reality twice the estimated value and one where it was assumed that the elasticity in each of the sectors is only one half of the estimated value.

Table 6-19
Shadow Prices on Capacity Expansion for the Monopoly Model
(Mills per kWh)

Region	*Year*	*Hydroelectric Plants*	*Fossil-fueled Plants*	*Nuclear Plants*
1. New England	1970	10.21	0.0	0.16
	1975	7.65	0.0	0.0
	1980	5.82	0.0	0.0
	1985	4.03	0.0	0.0
	1990	2.19	0.0	0.0
2. Middle Atlantic	1970	10.74	0.0	0.0
	1975	8.20	0.0	0.0
	1980	6.41	0.0	0.0
	1985	4.66	0.0	0.0
	1990	3.00	0.0	0.0
3. East North Central	1970	10.62	0.0	0.16
	1975	8.07	0.0	0.0
	1980	6.27	0.0	0.0
	1985	4.51	0.0	0.0
	1990	2.70	0.0	0.0
4. West North Central	1970	9.85	0.0	0.17
	1975	7.27	0.0	0.0
	1980	5.42	0.0	0.0
	1985	3.61	0.0	0.0
	1990	1.76	0.0	0.0
5. South Atlantic	1970	9.39	0.0	0.27
	1975	6.77	0.0	0.07
	1980	4.90	0.0	0.0
	1985	3.06	0.0	0.0
	1990	1.23	0.0	0.0
6. East South Central	1970	10.03	0.0	0.23
	1975	7.42	0.0	0.0
	1980	5.58	0.0	0.0
	1985	3.76	0.0	0.0
	1990	2.04	0.0	0.0
7. West South Central	1970	8.22	0.0	0.28
	1975	5.54	0.0	0.09
	1980	3.61	0.0	0.0
	1985	1.72	0.0	0.0
	1990	0.0	0.0	0.0
8. Mountain	1970	8.19	0.0	0.20
	1975	5.44	0.0	0.0
	1980	3.44	0.0	0.0
	1985	1.47	0.0	0.0
	1990	0.0	0.0	0.0
9. Pacific	1970	0.0	0.0	0.0
	1975	0.0	0.0	0.0
	1980	0.0	0.0	0.0
	1985	0.0	0.0	0.0
	1990	0.0	0.0	0.0

For the case where one half the elasticity estimate is used for each of the sectors across all regions, there is a very slight decline in the price of electrical energy (10 percent or less depending on the region) because of a reduction in the quantity demanded at any given price. With the reduction in the quantity demanded, a smaller amount of new capacity is needed and adherence to the marginal cost pricing concept dictates that the price should be lower. Interregional flows remain intact, though they are reduced in this case by about 50 percent.

For the situation in which twice the elasticity estimate is used for each of the sectors across all regions, there is an increase in the price of electrical energy (about 5 to 10 percent) because of the increase in the quantity of electrical energy demanded. There is some room for the expansion of new capacity so that no additional penalty exists because of meeting all of the capacity constraints. For example, in the West North Central Region in 1975, no fossil-fueled capacity was added in the previously solved perfectly competitive model. If the elasticity were twice as great, an additional 30.58 billion kWh of new fossil-fueled capacity would be installed. Interregional flows remain and increase around 40 to 60 percent. Moreover, one observes additional interregional flows of electrical energy from the West South Central region to the East North Central region in 1975 and from the West South Central region to the East North Central region in 1980.

In conclusion, if the elasticity in all sectors is twice that estimated, the results of the model more intensely favor a unified view of the market for electrical energy and hence strengthen the results with regard to the efficiency discussions. If the elasticity is only one half that estimated, the foregoing results are not markedly altered.

7 Conclusions

This study set out to look at the pricing and allocation of electrical energy in the United States by focusing on a unified market. Congruent with this look has been the realization that, for electrical energy, development planning is a continuous and sequential process involving mobilization and efficient use of resources. The important aspect of development planning in the electrical energy sector is the formulation of suitable policies to carry out the economic activities of generating, transmitting and distributing, and consuming over time and over space. Within the dimensions of the model, it has been shown that opportunities exist for increasing the efficiency of pricing and allocating electrical energy if regulatory commissions more judiciously adhere to a maxim of perfect competition when determining the rate schedule for electrical energy.

On June 4, 1971, the President of the United States in a message to Congress stressed the need to get back on the road to using our energy resources with increasing efficiency both at the point of production and at the point of consumption.[1] He continued by discussing the need to price energy on the basis of its costs to society. Within the model developed, it has been shown what the price profile should resemble over the next twenty years to move towards this proffered efficiency.

One cost that has not been explicitly included (except in the calculation of the capital cost of new generating capacity) is the cost incurred due to environmental constraints. Such things as air pollution control at stationary sources, waste heat dissipation, and disposal of recovered uranium from nuclear generation are absent from the model. These considerations will be included in subsequent work with this model.

More than two decades ago, Philip Sporn published a short monograph on the integrated power system.[2] In summary he stated:

(a) An adequate and economical supply of electrical energy is one of the elements needed to give a balanced economy to a region.

(b) The integrated power system has come to be recognized as the soundest basic mechanism for developing and for making available an adequate and economical power-supply system.

(c) Since power development is only one of the many phases of resource development, it should aim at the same social and economic objectives: the development and conservation of all resources so as to attain a more judicious use for the improvement of life and living.

These conclusions are as valid today as they were when first enunciated. From these considerations springs the essential need to have efficient pricing and allocating of electrical energy. It would be unreasonable to expect this efficiency to materialize instantaneously. However, it is not unreasonable to expect a movement towards an efficient allocation and determination of price of electrical energy.

General Conclusions

The model that has been developed has incorporated the salient points, with possibly a few exceptions, needed to make meaningful statements about the efficiency of generating, pricing, and allocating electrical energy. The results are not meant to be absolute in themselves but are an indication of the direction in which current considerations should move. The study possesses limitations that need to be carefully delimited before any final decisions are implemented. With this in mind, an abbreviated summary of the conclusions is presented.

The most obvious conclusion is that a misallocation of electrical energy among consuming sectors intraregionally exists. By virtue of the fact that the price of electrical energy is too high for the residential and commercial sectors and too low for the industrial sector, the industrial sector is consuming and is projected to continue to consume a greater quantity, if the projected price structure prevails, than the optimum would allow, while the residential and commercial sectors are consuming and are expected to continue to consume less than what would be optimal in an efficiency sense. The model is not constructed to show explicitly the welfare loss arising from the misallocation. However, to show the cost to society of this misallocation, it would only be necessary to compute the net social payoff given the prevailing and projected price structure across sectors for each region. A comparison of this value with the amount presented in the discussion of limited interregional flows in chapter 6 would give a measure of the welfare loss.

Second, the welfare of society could be enhanced if electrical energy industry development and operation were carried out by the utilities on a national basis, where it would be possible for all regions to take advantage of the economic efficiencies that one possesses in the generation of electrical energy. The desirability of interregional coordination has been shown to exist to a limited extent. It is felt that a higher degree of spatial resolution and a regional disaggregation of short-run marginal cost would strengthen this conclusion. Unfortunately, adequate data are not currently available to allow this refinement to be made.

Third, given that past output/capital ratios prevail in the future, there will be a tendency to invest too heavily in new generating capacity assuming that the regional estimates of the Federal Power Commission of additions of new capacity by plant type serve not only as the upper bound on capacity additions but also as the lower bound. In other words, if one is to interpret these values as the most likely additions to new generating capacity,[3] there will be a degree of wastefulness in investment in new fossil-fueled steam-electric generating capacity and a lesser degree of wasteful investment in new nuclear steam-electric generating capacity. This remark must be tempered by the recognition that the values used serve not as the probable additions but only as a constraint. If, as demand fails to expand to utilize currently existing capacity, the electrical energy industry alters its investment plans accordingly, wasteful investment will be mitigated.

Fourth, in conjunction with the foregoing observation, one can explicitly measure the cost to society due to expansion limitations of new generating capacity. It is to society's general advantage to expand generating capacity of the least expensive plant type first. If approximately the same capital cost prevails for additions to capacity beyond the physical, institutional, and technological limitations existing (i.e., if the limitations can be reasonably pushed outward), a concerted effort should be made to undertake such an expansion. Thus, in the case of hydroelectric plants, if only modest increases in expenditures are needed for altering current physical conditions of the landscape or for undertaking fruitful research and development, then such increased expenditure is justified, conditional upon the benefit (a reduction in the penalty incurred) outweighing the cost. Alternately, other generating methods might be investigated more intensely if it is expected that capital costs can be made to compare favorably to the more traditional plant types. Geothermal generation was mentioned above. Solar generation is another as yet untapped resource that might eventually prove to have investment and operation and maintenance costs in the range now existing for hydroelectric generation.

Finally, the electrical energy industry, even when the average price paid by all sectors in a region is considered, does not follow and is not expected to follow a marginal cost pricing rule. Put crudely, marginal cost pricing means paying for assets when they are being used, not before they are acquired. It is fairly evident from chapter 6 that the electrical energy industry is charging and, matter-of-factly, will continue to charge a price in excess of the marginal cost of supplying electrical energy. A calculation of the welfare loss to society due to the current inefficient pricing scheme could be performed by computing the net social payoff under the existing and projected prices and under the optimal prices and comparing the two values. This would give a quantitative measure of the inefficiency. The important point with regard to the bold departure from marginal cost pricing, though, is that there is no attempt even to approximate the allocative efficiency criterion.

A Consummatory Remark

It cannot be stressed too strongly or too many times that the results of this analysis are to be viewed in light of many inherent limitations in the study. The estimations of the parameters of demand (whether as fixed points or in functional form) and cost relations can be improved still further if a greater quantity of more reliable information is made available. For more comprehensive generation, allocation, and price policy decisions, a detailed study of this kind in the broader perspective of the total energy picture is needed. Nevertheless, within its limited scope, this study has generated information helpful in analyzing normatively an efficient price-output situation under free and controlled market conditions for electrical energy. Also this study has employed certain modifications in the original intertemporal-spatial price equilibrium model such as the inclusion of different types of generation of electrical energy, an investment allocation process, and an explicit measurement of penalties involved due to physical, institutional, and technological limitations on various types of generating capacity additions. These modifications have heretofore not been incorporated in a model of this type. The validity and usefulness of these modifications as a guide to decision makers are proved in this study.

Appendix
Detailed Cost Analysis

A more detailed treatment of the analytical method used in CONCEPT is presented below. The mathematical equations are presented for those who wish to understand the basic method and as an aid for using special options. Most of this discussion is concerned with the extrapolation of base costs (or reference costs) to other sizes, the adjustment of costs from a base year and base location to a new year and new location, the projection of cost index data, the escalation of costs during the design and construction period, and the calculation of interest during construction.

The two-digit account direct costs for the base cost model are scaled by equations that describe the costs as a function of plant capacity. These equations are of the form

$$C_i = \alpha_i + \beta_i \left(\frac{X}{X_b} \right)^{\gamma i} \quad \text{(A.1)}$$

where C_i is the total direct cost for each two-digit account i for a plant of X net electrical capacity and X_b is the base plant size. The coefficients α_i, β_i, and γ_i are determined by fitting equation (A.1) by ordinary least squares. These coefficients are different for each type of plant and are stored on the cost model tape. For simplification, the subscript i will be omitted in most of the subsequent equations.

Each total two-digit account direct cost is subdivided into costs for equipment, labor, and materials for the base year and base location by equations of the form

$$C_j = CF_j \quad \text{(A.2)}$$

where C_j is the cost component for each two-digit account direct cost at the base year and base location, and F_j is a factor calculated from cost model data and is used for dividing the costs into the three components at the two-digit account level. Each factor F_j is calculated as

$$F_j = \frac{C_{jb}}{C_b} \quad \text{(A.3)}$$

where C_{jb} is the cost of equipment, labor, or materials for j = 1, 2, 3, respectively, at the two-digit account level for the base cost model and C_b is the total cost of the two-digit account for the base cost model. The base costs C_{jb} are stored on the cost model tape.

The cost index data are used for adjusting the subdivided capital costs from the base time and base location to costs at other cities and for escalating costs to other years. The historical data, except labor productivity, are extrapolated exponentially by the following equation:

$$I = \overline{C}_f(1 + \overline{\epsilon})^{Y-Y_f} \tag{A.4}$$

where I is a projected cost index for the year Y for each of the three cost components of each two-digit account, Y_f is a reference year for historical cost index data, and $\overline{C}_f$ and $\overline{\epsilon}$ are coefficients retrieved from the cost model.

The equation for projecting labor productivity indexes has the following form:

$$P = \rho + \mu(Y - Y_b) \tag{A.5}$$

where P is a productivity index in the year Y for the labor component of each two-digit account, Y_b is the base year associated with the base cost model, and ρ and μ are coefficients specified by the user at program execution time. Default values are $\rho = 1$ and $\mu = 0$, so labor productivity is constant with time and location unless otherwise specified by the user.

The subdivided costs C_j calculated by equation (A.2) for the base year Y_b and base location are adjusted to costs C_j^* for a new year Y_s and new location by using the cost and productivity indexes calculated by equations (A.4) and (A.5). Equipment and materials cost ($j = 1$ and 3 respectively) are calculated by equation (A.6) and labor costs ($j = 2$) by equation (A.7):

$$C_j^* = C_j \frac{I_j^*}{I_j} \tag{A.6}$$

$$C_2^* = C_2 \frac{I_2^*}{I_2} \frac{P}{P^*} \frac{B^*}{B} \tag{A.7}$$

where I_j^* and I_j are cost indexes, P^* and P are labor productivity indexes, and B^* and B are factors that reflect the contractor's overhead burden on craft labor for the new year Y_s and new location and base year Y_b and base location respectively.

Site man-hours H^* for each two-digit account are calculated with the following equation:

$$H^* = \frac{C_2^*}{R^* B^*} \tag{A.8}$$

where C_2^* is the labor cost component for each two-digit account from equation (A.7), R^* is the hourly wage rate for each two-digit account and is identical with the cost index I_2^* for labor in equation (A.7), and B^* is the burden factor in equation (A.7).

If an overtime workweek is specified, the labor costs for each two-digit account are adjusted by an overtime efficiency E and an average hourly wage rate ratio ϕ, defined as

$$E = 1 + [\eta(W - 40)] \quad \text{(A.9)}$$

and

$$\phi = \frac{40 + [T(W - 40)]}{W} \quad \text{(A.10)}$$

where W is the total workweek in hours, η is a constant determined by fitting equation (A.9) to the overtime efficiency curve, and T is the ratio of the hourly rate for overtime to the hourly rate for straight time.

When overtime is specified, the labor cost component $C^*_{2,o}$ and man-hours H^*_o for each two-digit account for the new year and location are calculated by modifying the straight-time costs and man-hours, equations (A.7) and (A.8), as follows:

$$C^*_{2,o} = C^*_2 \frac{\phi}{E} \quad \text{(A.7a)}$$

and

$$H^*_o = H^* \frac{1}{E} \quad \text{(A.8a)}$$

The analysis described to this point in equation (A.1) through (A.10) and (A.7a) and (A.8a) gives the direct cost components at the two-digit account level for the input plant at the year of start of the design and construction period, Y_s. The next step is to calculate escalation during the construction period. The direct cost components, equipment, labor, and materials, are each escalated separately at the two-digit account level. The calculations are accomplished by dividing the design and construction period into discrete time steps, evaluating the cash flow for each cost component in each time step, and summing the stepwise cash flows. Cumulative cash flow curves are utilized for defining cash expenditures as a function of time.

The escalated costs C^{**}_j of both equipment and materials (j = 1 and 3) are found by multiplying the costs C^*_j at the start of construction by the ratio of the average cost index $\overline{I^{**}_j}$ during the design and construction period to the cost index I^*_j at the start of the design and construction period, as follows:

$$C^{**}_j = C_j^* \frac{\overline{I^{**}_j}}{I^*_j} \quad \text{(A.11)}$$

where

$$\overline{I^{**}_j} = \sum_{y=Y^*_s}^{Ye} I_j\,(y)\,\Delta f\,(y) \quad \text{(A.12)}$$

and $I_j(y)$ is the cost index for year y and $\Delta f(y)$ is an incremental cash flow at time y; Y_e is the end of the construction period.

The escalated costs C_2^{**} when (or $C_{2,o}^{**}$ when overtime is specified) of labor are calculated in a similar manner, and, in addition, labor productivity P^* at start of design and construction and the average productivity $\overline{P^{**}}$ must be considered, as follows:

$$C_2^{**} = C_2^* \frac{P^* \ \overline{I_2^{**}}}{I_2^* \ \overline{P^{**}}} \qquad \text{(A.13)}$$

where

$$\frac{\overline{I_2^{**}}}{\overline{P^{**}}} = \sum_{y=Y_s^*}^{Ye} \frac{I_2(y)}{P(y)} \Delta f(y) \qquad \text{(A.14)}$$

where $P(y)$ is the productivity index for year y and the other terms are as defined for equations (A.11) and (A.12).

The general equations for calculating the three-, four-, and five-digit account costs, which follow, are applied either to costs C_j^* at start of construction Y_s or to costs C_j^{**} at end of construction Y_e. The equations for end of construction are shown below; those for start of construction are similar.

$$C_{j,3}^{**} = C_j^{**} F_{j,3} \qquad \text{(A.15)}$$

$$C_{j,4}^{**} = C_{j,3}^{**} F_{j,4} \qquad \text{(A.16)}$$

and

$$C_{j,5}^{**} = C_{j,4}^{**} F_{j,5} \qquad \text{(A.17)}$$

where C_j^{**}, $C_{j,3}^{**}$, $C_{j,4}^{**}$, and $C_{j,5}^{**}$ are the cost components at the end of design and construction for equipment, labor, and materials ($j = 1$, 2, and 3) at the two-, three-, four-, and five-digit account levels, respectively, and $F_{j,3}$, $F_{j,4}$, and $F_{j,5}$ are factors, calculated from base cost model data, which are used for defining the subdivided cost components at the three-, four-, and five-digit account levels respectively.

The factors $F_{j,3}$, $F_{j,4}$, and $F_{j,5}$ are defined as

$$F_{j,3} = \frac{C_{jb,3}}{C_{jb}} \qquad \text{(A.18)}$$

$$F_{j,4} = \frac{C_{jb,4}}{C_{jb,3}} \qquad \text{(A.19)}$$

and

$$F_{j,5} = \frac{C_{jb,5}}{C_{jb,4}} \qquad \text{(A.20)}$$

where C_{jb}, $C_{jb,3}$, $C_{jb,4}$, $C_{jb,5}$ are cost components for equipment, labor, and materials at the two-, three-, four-, and five-digit levels, respectively, for the base cost model.

The direct costs at the three-, four-, and five-digit account levels are now resummed to the two-digit account level. Spare parts and contingency allowances are then calculated as percentages of equipment and materials costs and labor costs for each two-digit account and summed over all two-digit direct cost accounts as follows:

$$C_k = \sum C_j^{**} F_{jk} \tag{A.21}$$

and

$$C_{jm} = \sum C_j^{**} F_{jm} \tag{A.22}$$

where C_k and C_{jm} are the total spare parts and contingency allowances, respectively, and F_{jk} and F_{jm} are the multiplication factors for each two-digit account.

Indirect costs, except interest during construction, are calculated via curves which are functions of total direct costs and have the following general form:

$$F(Z) = \kappa + \frac{\lambda}{(\omega + Z)^{\tau}} \tag{A.23}$$

where Z is the appropriate direct cost and κ, λ, ω, τ are coefficients evaluated by fitting equation (A.23) to the appropriate curve.

The total cost I_T of interest during construction is calculated in two parts, interest on two-digit account direct costs and interest on associated indirect costs, as shown in the following procedure.

Interest I_i on each two-digit direct cost account i is calculated as a function of the cash flow of that account, using normalized cash flow curves. Consider the normalized cash flow curve for an account i. The cost ΔI_i of interest paid on an amount of money $C_i f_i(y)$ in time Δy is

$$\Delta I_i = C_i f_i(y)\ R(y)\ \Delta_y \tag{A.24}$$

where C_i is the total cost of account i, $f_i(y)$ is a normalized cash flow at time y, and $R(y)$ is the interest rate as a function of time. Therefore the total interest paid on the total cost C_i of an account will be the sum of ΔI_i's over the applicable time period, $Y_e - Y_{si}^*$. The value for Y_{si}^* is, in general, equal to Y_s; however, the time periods for the various two-digit direct cost accounts are not necessarily the same. Hence, the design and construction period, $Y_e - Y_s$, can be modified with a lead time T_{li} for each account, which, in the cost model is set equal to zero for all accounts except land and special materials.

Land is assumed to be bought one year prior to the start of design and construction Y_s, and special materials, such as the helium coolant for

HTGR plants, are assumed to be bought one year prior to commercial operation Y_e. The following development allows the general inclusion of lead times where a two-digit account cash flow can be modified through NAMELIST input at problem execution. The general definition of the time periods, $Y_e - Y_{si}^*$, for each two-digit account is expressed by the following equation, where T_i is equal to $Y_e - Y_{si}^*$:

$$T_i = \begin{cases} Y_e - Y_s + T_{li}, & T_{li} \geq 0 \\ |T_{li}|, & T_{li} < 0 \end{cases} \tag{A.25}$$

The total cost of interest for each two-digit direct cost account is given by

$$I_i = C_i \sum_{y=Y_s^* i}^{Ye} f_i(y)\, R(y)\, \Delta y \tag{A.26}$$

The interest can be compounded by simply adding the cost of interest, $I_i(y - \Delta y)$, for each Δy into the summation. This is an option via normal input data.

$$I_i = \sum_{y=Ysi^*}^{Ye} [C_i + I_i(y - \Delta y)]\, f_i(y)\, R(y)\, \Delta y \tag{A.26a}$$

The total cost of interest during construction is

$$I_T = \sum_{i=1}^{N} [I_i + C_i \bar{f}\, \overline{DR}] \tag{A.27}$$

where for simple interest,

$$\overline{DR} = \bar{R}(Y_e - Y_s) \tag{A.28}$$

and for compound interest,

$$\overline{DR} = (1 + \bar{R})^{Y_e - Y_s} - 1 \tag{A.28a}$$

where $\bar{R}$ is the average interest rate during the period $Y_e - Y_s$, N is the number of two-digit direct cost accounts, I_i and C_i are as defined previously, and $\bar{f}$ is a multiplier developed from the two-digit account cash flow curves defined as follows:

$$\bar{f} = \frac{\sum_{i=1}^{N} C_i \sum_{y=Ys}^{Ye} f_i(y)\, \Delta y}{\sum_{i=1}^{N} C_i\, [f_i(Y_e) - f_i(Y_s)]} \tag{A.29}$$

where $f_i(y)$ is the cumulative cash flow at year y, Δy is a differential time period, and $f_i(Y_e)$ and $f_i(Y_s)$ are cumulative cash flows at end and start of construction respectively.

Finally, all costs, including costs of land, physical plant direct costs, spare parts, contingencies, indirects, and interest during construction, are summed to give the total capital cost of the plant.

Notes

Chapter 1
Introduction

1. Committee on Interior and Insular Affairs, *Summary Report of the Cornell Workshop on Energy and the Environment,* U.S. Senate, 92nd Congress, 2nd Session, May 1972, p. 147.

2. By 1990 about 41 percent of all raw energy consumption (on a heat basis) in the country is expected to be used to generate electrical energy.

3. Donella Meadows et al., *The Limits to Growth: A Report for the Club of Rome's Project on the Predicament of Mankind,* New American Library, New York, 1972.

4. A model that endeavors to look at an efficient allocation of all energy sources, and not just electrical energy, is that developed by W.D. Nordhaus in the "The Allocation of Energy Resources," *Brookings Papers on Economic Activity 3,* 1973, pp. 529-570.

5. M.S. Feldstein in "Equity and Efficiency in Public Sector Pricing: The Optimal Two-Part Tariff," *The Quarterly Journal of Economics,* vol. 86, no. 2 (May 1972) shows how equity considerations might be included in a model very similar to the one that will be developed here.

6. For a more extensive discussion of these ideas, see F.A. Beer, "Energy, Environment, and International Integration," in *Growing Against Ourselves,* S.L. Kwee (ed.), Lexington Books, D.C. Heath and Company, Lexington, Mass., 1972.

7. Committee on Interstate and Foreign Commerce, *Power Plant Siting and Environmental Protection. Part I,* U.S. House of Representatives, 92nd Congress, 1st Session, May 1971, p. 89. As a postscript, this piece of legislation died in committee during the 92nd Congress.

8. Mr. VanDeerlin (41st District, California), a sponsor of the bill, indicated this in a letter of January 21, 1974. A similar bill in the Senate, S. 357, seems destined for the same fate.

9. See the first essay of T. Koopmans in *Three Essays on the State of Economic Science,* McGraw-Hill Book Company, New York, 1957 and Y. Plessner, "Activity Analysis, Quadratic Programming, and General Equilibrium," *International Economic Review,* vol. 8, no. 2 (June 1967), pp. 168-179.

10. S. Enke, "Equilibrium Among Spatially Separated Markets, Solution by Electric Analogue," *Econometrica,* vol. 19, no. 1 (January 1951), pp. 40-47.

11. P.A. Samuelson's formulation is in his "Spatial Price Equilibrium and Linear Programming," *American Economic Review,* vol. 42 (June 1952), pp. 283-303. This work draws on T. Koopmans's discussion in *Activity Analysis of Production and Allocation,* John Wiley & Sons, New York, 1951, pp. 229-259 and pp. 359-373.

12. T. Takayama and G.G. Judge, "Equilibrium Among Spatially Separated Markets: A Reformulation," *Econometrica,* vol. 32, no. 4 (October 1964), pp. 510-524.

13. T. Takayama and A.D. Woodland, "Equivalence of Price and Quantity Formulations of Spatial Equilibrium: Purified Duality in Quadratic and Concave Programming," *Econometrica,* vol. 38, no. 6 (November 1970), pp. 889-906.

14. P.A. Samuelson, "Intertemporal Price Equilibrium: A Prologue to the Theory of Speculation," *Weltwirtschaftliches Archiv,* vol. 79 (1957), pp. 181-221.

15. T. Takayama and G.G. Judge, "An Intertemporal Price Equilibrium Model," *Journal of Farm Economics,* vol. 46, no. 2 (May 1964), pp. 477-486.

16. The whole controversy is summarized in J.M. Currie, J.A. Murphy, and A. Schmitz, "The Concept of Economic Surplus and Its Use in Economic Analysis," *The Economic Journal,* vol. 81, no. 324 (December 1971), pp. 741-799.

17. J. Bhagwati, "The Pure Theory of International Trade: A Survey," by American Economic Association and Royal Economic Society, *Surveys of Economic Theory, Volume 2,* St. Martins Press, New York, 1965, p. 213.

18. T. Takayama and G.G. Judge, *Spatial and Temporal Price and Allocation Models,* North-Holland Publishing Company, Amsterdam, 1971, p. 34.

19. J. Henderson and R.E. Quandt, *Microeconomic Theory,* 2nd. ed., McGraw-Hill Book Company, New York, 1971, pp. 255-264.

20. T.C. Lee and S.K. Seaver, "A Positive Model of Spatial Equilibrium with Special Reference to the Broiler Markets," in *Studies in Economic Planning Over Space and Time,* G.G. Judge and T. Takayama (eds.), North-Holland Publishing Company, Amsterdam, 1973, p. 443.

21. Haavelmo says that a most dangerous procedure in estimating parameters in a system of stochastic equations is to fit each equation separately without regard to the fact that the variables involved are usually assumed to satisfy, simultaneously, a number of other stochastic relations. T. Haavelmo, "The Statistical Implications of a System of Simultaneous Equations," *Econometrica,* vol. 11, no. 1 (January 1943), p. 2.

22. C. Wilcox, *Public Policies Toward Business,* Richard D. Irwin,

Homewood, Ill. 1971, pp. 356-360. This reference gives a brief but complete discussion of electrical energy regulation.

23. A. Kahn, *The Economics of Regulation, Volume 1,* John Wiley & Sons, New York, 1970, p. 17.

24. F.M. Scherer, *Industrial Market Structure and Economic Performance,* Rand-McNally & Company, Chicago, 1970, p. 521-523.

25. *Ibid.*, pp. 72-78.

26. *Ibid.,* pp. 88-90.

27. C.J. Cicchetti and W.J. Gillin, "Electricity Growth: Economic Incentives and Environmental Quality," reprinted in *Energy Conservation,* Committee on Interior and Insular Affairs, U.S. Senate, 93rd Congress, 1st Session, March 22 and 23, 1973, pp. 186-7.

28. H.O. Nourse, *Regional Economics,* McGraw-Hill Book Company, New York, 1968, p. 131.

29. Federal Power Commission, *The 1970 National Power Survey,* U.S. Government Printing Office, Washington, December 1971, p. I-8-1.

30. *Ibid.,* p. I-1-6.

Chapter 2
Estimation of Demand

1. T. Takayama and G.G. Judge, *Spatial and Temporal Price and Allocation Models,* North-Holland Publishing Company, Amsterdam, 1971, p. 333.

2. E.J. Working, "What Do Statistical 'Demand Curves' Show?" *Quarterly Journal of Economics,* vol. 41 (May 1927), pp. 212-235.

3. J.L. Bridge, *Applied Econometrics,* North-Holland Publishing Company, Amsterdam, 1971, p. 99.

4. H.S. Houthakker, "Additive Preferences," *Econometrica,* vol. 28, no. 2 (April 1960), pp. 249-252.

5. H.S. Houthakker, "New Evidence on Demand Elasticities," *Econometrica,* vol. 33, no. 2 (April 1965), p. 278. Though Houthakker is not referring explicitly to the functional form adopted here, his comments are still relevant.

6. J.S. Cramer, *Empirical Econometrics,* North-Holland Publishing Company, Amsterdam, 1971, p. 213.

7. Marc Nerlove, "Returns to Scale in Electricity Supply," in *Readings in Economic Statistics and Econometrics,* A. Zellner (ed.), Little, Brown and Company, Boston, 1968, p. 410.

8. The dependent variable has a strong trend component. In fact when

each sector for each region was looked at separately, more than 90 percent of all variation was explained by trend alone.

9. Edwin Kuh, "The Validity of Cross Sectionally Estimated Behavior Equations in Time Series Applications," *Econometrica,* vol. 27, no. 2 (April 1959), p. 200.

10. Carl Christ, *Econometric Models and Methods,* John Wiley & Sons, New York, 1966, p. 457.

11. R.E. Baxter and R. Rees, "Analysis of the Industrial Demand for Electricity," *The Economic Journal,* vol. 78, no. 310 (June 1968), p. 284.

12. Henri Theil, "Specification Errors and the Estimation of Economic Relationships," *Review of the International Statistical Institute,* vol. 25, no. 1/3 (1957), p. 43.

13. Zvi Griliches, "Distributed Lags: A Survey," *Econometrica,* vol. 35, no. 1 (January 1967), p. 38.

14. T.D. Mount, L.D. Chapman, and T.J. Tyrrell, *Electricity Demand in the United States: An Econometric Analysis,* Oak Ridge National Laboratory, ORNL-NSF-EP-49, June 1973, p. 3.

15. Arnold Zellner, "An Efficient Method of Estimating Seemingly Unrelated Regressions and Tests for Aggregation Bias," *The Journal of the American Statistical Association,* vol. 57 (June 1962), pp. 348-368.

16. P. Balestra and Marc Nerlove, "Pooling Cross Section and Time Series Data in the Estimation of a Dynamic Model: The Demand for Natural Gas," *Econometrica,* vol. 34, no. 3 (July 1966), p. 594. While Balestra and Nerlove do not include this third component, subsequent work included it. See for example V.K. Chetty, "Pooling of Time Series and Cross Section Data," *Econometrica,* vol. 36, no. 2 (April 1968), p. 280.

17. H.S. Perloff, E.S. Dunn, E.S. Lampard, and R.F. Muth, *Regions, Resources, and Economic Growth,* University of Nebraska Press, Lincoln, 1960, p. 452.

18. Texas Eastern Transmission Corporation, *Competition and Growth in the American Energy Markets 1947-1985,* Texas Eastern Transmission Corporation, Houston, 1968, p. 31.

19. H. Houthakker, P. Verlager, and D.P. Sheehan, "Dynamic Demand Analysis for Gasoline and Residential Electricity," Paper presented at the American Economic Association Meetings, New York, December 1973.

20. Alternatively, the constant term in the equation could have been set to zero and nine dummy variables employed. Since the constraints are merely different constraints imposed on the model, they will yield identical estimates of $\log y^*_{ijt}$ and while the direct interpretation of the two versions differ, estimates for one are readily derived from those obtained for the

other. See D.B. Suits, "Use of Dummy Variables in Regression Equations," *The Journal of the American Statistical Association,* vol. 52 (December 1957), p. 549.

21. Arthur S. Goldberger, *Econometric Theory,* John Wiley & Sons, New York, 1964, p. 271.

22. Nissan Liviatan, "Consistent Estimation of Distributed Lags," *International Economic Review,* vol. 4, no. 1 (January 1963), p. 47.

23. The average price is the quotient of electrical energy (gas) revenues divided by sales of electrical energy (gas).

24. John W. Wilson, "Residential Demand for Electricity," *The Quarterly Review of Economics and Business,* vol. 11, no. 1 (Spring 1971), pp. 7-19.

25. *Ibid.*, p. 13.

26. Michael K. Evans, *Macroeconomic Activity: Theory, Forecasting, and Control,* Harper and Row Publishers, New York, 1969, p. 55.

27. *Ibid.*, p. 56. Also notice that kWh is a physical measure of electrical energy.

28. H.S. Houthakker and P. Verlager, "The Demand for Gasoline: A Mixed Cross Sectional and Time Series Analysis," Unpublished, May 1973, p. 9.

29. J. Kmenta, *Elements of Econometrics,* Macmillan Company, New York, 1971, p. 379.

30. The implicit supposition is that all the exogenous variables will attain some equilibrium level.

31. Available methods of mitigating the problem are covered in P.J. Dhrymes, *Distributed Lags: Problems of Estimation and Formulation,* Holden-Day, San Francisco, 1971, pp. 109-126.

32. Franklin Fisher and Carl Kaysen, *A Study in Econometrics: The Demand for Electricity in the United States,* North-Holland Publishing Company, Amsterdam, 1962, p. 118.

33. There are other factors influencing this demand. However, the price of output and the effective demand are the most important. See J. Henderson and R.E. Quandt, *Microeconomic Theory,* 2nd ed., McGraw-Hill Book Company, New York, 1971, p. 127.

34. Preliminary analysis, where different specifications were tried, consistently yielded the corresponding positive and negative coefficients on the variables ultimately included in the model.

35. Mount, et al., *Electricity Demand,* pp. 1-11.

36. Fisher and Kaysen, *Demand for Electricity.*

37. Mount, et al., provides a summary of these previous studies on p. 5.

38. See Wilson's criticisms in the *Quarterly Review* article, pp. 8-11.

39. Goldberger, *Econometric Theory,* p. 192.

40. R.G.D. Allen, *Mathematical Economics,* St. Martin's Press, New York, 1960, p. 694.

41. Y. Grunfeld and Zvi Griliches, "Is Aggregation Necessarily Bad?" *The Review of Economics and Statistics,* vol. 42 (February 1960), pp. 1-13.

42. A. Madansky, "The Fitting of Straight Lines When Both Variables Are Subject to Error," *The Journal of the American Statistical Association,* vol. 54 (March 1959), p. 175.

43. This is implicit in the higher average use rate.

44. Oran Culberson, *The Consumption of Electricity in the United States,* Oak Ridge National Laboratory, ORNL-NSF-EP-5, June 1971, p. 18.

45. *Ibid.,* p. 20.

46. R.D. Doctor, K.P. Anderson, M.B. Berman, S.H. Dole, M.J. Hammer, P.T. McClure, and C.D. Smith, *California's Electricity Quandary: III Slowing the Growth Rate,* Rand Corporation, Santa Monica, R-1116-NSF/CSA, September 1972, p. 30.

47. *Ibid.,* p. 78.

48. Fisher and Kaysen, *Demand for Electricity,* p. 120.

49. K.P. Anderson, *Toward Econometric Estimation of Industrial Energy Demand: An Experimental Application to the Primary Metals Industry,* Rand Corporation, Santa Monica, R-719-NSF, December 1971, p. 24.

50. Doctor, et al., *Electricity Quandary,* p. 88.

51. Mount, et al., *Electricity Demand,* p. 16.

Chapter 3
Future Demand for Electrical Energy

1. Henri Theil, *Applied Economic Forecasting*, Rand-McNally & Company, Chicago, 1966, p. 5.

2. This section draws heavily from the Committee on Interior and Insular Affairs, *Energy "Demand" Studies: An Analysis and Appraisal*, U.S. House of Representatives, 92nd Congress, 2nd Session, September 1972, pp. 49-51.

3. Henri Theil, *Economic Forecasts and Policy*, 2nd ed., North-Holland Publishing Company, Amsterdam, 1965, p. 15.

4. Committee on Interior and Insular Affairs, *Survey of Energy Consumption Projections*, U.S. Senate, 92nd Congress, 2nd Session, 1972, p. 18.

5. Federal Power Commission, *The 1970 National Power Survey*, U.S. Government Printing Office, Washington, December 1971, p. I-3-4.

6. Theil, *Applied Economic Forecasting*, p. 6.

7. The econometrics of the problem are discussed in Henri Theil, *Principles of Econometrics*, John Wiley & Sons, New York, 1971, pp. 122-124.

8. *Ibid.*, p. 123.

9. Theil, *Applied Economic Forecasting*, pp. 9-10.

10. This whole approach follows closely the work of D. Chapman, T. Tyrrell, and T. Mount, "Electricity Demand Growth and the Energy Crisis," *Science*, vol. 178 (November 19, 1972), pp. 703-708, and reference to this source will provide a broader background and explication of the undertaking.

11. R. E. Graham, Jr., H. C. Degraff, E. A. Trott, Jr., "State Projection of Income, Employment, and Population," *Survey of Current Business*, vol. 52, no. 4 (April 1972). The population figures were obtained from Table 4, p. 34, and the total personal income figures were obtained from Table 3, p. 33.

12. *Ibid.*, p. 28.

13. *Ibid.*, p. 26.

14. Leroy Culbertson, *Professional Engineer*, February 1971, p. 17. Mr. Culbertson is Vice President of the Gas and Gas Liquids Department of Phillips Petroleum Company.

15. R. M. Nixon, *Messages from the President of the United States Concerning Energy Resources*, U.S. Government Printing Office, Washington, April 18, 1973, p. 4.

16. Federal Power Commission, *Forecasts of Electric Energy and Demand to the Year 2000, A Report by the Task Force on Forecast Review to the Technical Advisory Committee on Power Supply, National Power Survey*, Appendix 4, Table VI, August 24, 1973.

17. Leonard M. Olmsted, "24th Annual Electrical Industry Forecast," *Electrical World*, September 15, 1973, p. 47.

18. *Ibid.*, p. 48.

19. Federal Power Commission, *1970 National Power Survey*, p. I-19-10.

20. W. D. Nordhaus, "The Allocation of Energy Resources," *Brookings Papers on Economic Activity 3*, 1973, p. 555.

21. Alternative possible assumptions concerning the increase of prices and per capita personal income are detailed in Tim Tyrrell and Duane Chapman, "Demand for Electricity: The Ohio Test Region and the United States (1970-2000)," Unpublished, August 1972, p. 9. It is felt that these assumptions are extreme and do not reflect the most likely course of events.

Chapter 4
Transmission, Distribution, and Supply Considerations

1. E. W. Shows and R. H. Burton, *Microeconomics*, Lexington Books, D. C. Heath and Company, Lexington, Mass., 1972, p. 182.

2. As in the case of natural gas (see L. Waverman, *Natural Gas and National Policy*, University of Toronto Press, Toronto, 1973, p. 31), the physical capacity of a transmission line is not a determinate number like K. Capacity can be increased by adding horsepower to a station, a station to the line, or by looping the line.

3. The average cost function (c_{ij}) is as follows:

$$c_{ij} = C_{ij}/x_{ij} = a + bs_{ij}/x_{ij}.$$

The marginal cost is simply a.

4. Federal Power Commission, *The 1970 National Power Survey*, U.S. Government Printing Office, Washington, December 1971, p. I-13-9.

5. *Ibid.*, pp. I-13-1-I-13-8.

6. *Ibid.*, p. I-14-1.

7. *Ibid.*, p. IV-3-68.

8. *Ibid.*, p. IV-3-70.

9. *Ibid.*, p. IV-14-5.

10. *Ibid.*, p. IV-3-78.

11. *Ibid.*, p. IV-3-77.

12. Though there are several articles and books dealing with returns to scale in electrical energy generation, the better ones are Y. Barzel, "The Production Function and Technical Change in the Steam Power Industry," *The Journal of Political Economy*, Vol. 72 (April 1964), P. J. Dhrymes and M. Kurz, "Technology and Scale in Electricity Generation," *Econometrica*, vol. 32, no. 3 (July 1964), R. Komiya, "Technological Progress and the Production Function in the United States Steam Power Industry," *The Review of Economics and Statistics*, vol. 44 (May 1962), M. Galatin, *Economies of Scale and Technological Change in Thermal Power Generation*, North-Holland Publishing Company, Amsterdam, 1968, and

M. Nerlove, *Estimation and Identification of Cobb-Douglas Production Functions*, Rand-McNally & Company, Chicago, 1965 (chapter VI).

13. This is a common, yet unrealistic, assumption. See, for example, chapter 3 of M. L. Baughman, *Dynamic Energy System Modeling*, Unpublished PhD. Thesis, M.I.T., August 1972.

14. Federal Power Commission, *Statistics of Privately Owned Electric Utilities in the United States, Classes A and B Companies*, U.S. Government Printing Office, Washington, October 1972.

15. Federal Power Commission, *1970 National Power Survey*, p. I-5-4.

16. Dennis Anderson, "Models for Determining Least Cost Investments in Electricity Supply," *The Bell Journal of Economics and Management Science*, vol. 3, no. 1 (Spring 1972), p. 271.

17. *Ibid.*, p. 268.

18. D. S. P. Hopkins, "Sufficient Conditions for Optimality in Infinite Horizon Linear Economic Models," Technical Report No. 69-3, Stanford University, 1969.

19. S. C. Littlechild, "Marginal Cost Pricing with Joint Costs," *The Economic Journal*, vol. 80, no. 318 (June 1970).

20. J. Henderson and R. E. Quandt, *Microeconomic Theory*, 2nd ed., McGraw-Hill Book Company, New York, 1971, p. 89.

21. *Ibid.*, p. 89.

22. *Ibid.*, p. 70.

23. Ralph Turvey, *Optimal Pricing and Investment in Electricity Supply*, George Allen and Unwin, London, 1968.

24. Ralph Turvey, "Marginal Cost," *The Economic Journal*, vol. 79, no. 314 (June 1969), pp. 282-99.

25. One constraint that is often employed but is not used at all in the current problem formulation is a limitation on profits. This does not mean that such a restriction cannot be used (i.e., by restricting total revenue minus total cost.) See I. Pressman, "A Mathematical Formulation of the Peak-Load Pricing Problem", *The Bell Journal of Economics and Management Science*, vol. 1, no. 2 (Autumn 1970), p. 311.

26. Leonard M. Olmsted, "24th Annual Electrical Industry Forecast," *Electrical World*, September 15, 1973, p. 51.

27. Thomas Duchesneau, *Interfuel Substitutibility in the Electric Utility Sector of the U. S. Economy*, U.S. Government Printing Office, Washington, February 1972.

28. Federal Power Commission, *Steam-Electric Plant Construction Cost and Annual Production Expenses, Twenty-Fourth Annual Supplement, 1971*, U.S. Government Printing Office, Washington, February 1973, pp. XIV-XVII.

29. M. Galatin, *Economies of Scale and Technological Change in Thermal Power Generation*, North-Holland Publishing Company, Amsterdam, 1968, chapter 4.

30. This comment is inserted as a prelude to later results where capital investment decisions are looked at from a regional standpoint.

31. Henderson and Quandt, *Microeconomic Theory*, p. 71.

32. Galatin, *Economies of Scale*.

33. A good discussion of the problems encountered in measuring the aggregate cost function with regard to technological change is found in R. M. Solow, "Technological Change and the Aggregate Production Function," *The Review of Economics and Statistics*, August 1957, pp. 312-320.

34. Federal Power Commission, *Steam-Electric Plant Construction Cost.*, Table 9, p. XXVIII.

35. An alternative that might be used as a measure of technological change is the factor productivity ratio developed by John Kendrick in *Postwar Productivity Trends in the United States, 1948-1969*, National Bureau of Economic Research, New York, 1973, pp. 349-350. Unfortunately, gas production is included in the measure, and the measure does not span the time period used for estimating the cost functions.

36. C. Christ, *Econometric Models and Methods*, John Wiley & Sons, New York, 1966, p. 457.

37. A fine exposition on technological progress can be found in J. Schmookler, "Economic Sources of Inventive Activity," *The Journal of Economic History*, March 1962, pp. 1-20.

38. J. Johnston, *Statistical Cost Analysis*, McGraw Hill Book Company, New York, 1960, p. 54.

39. *Ibid.*, p. 170.

40. J. Kmenta, *Elements of Econometrics*, Macmillan Company, New York, 1971, p. 586.

41. P. Dhrymes, *Econometrics*, Harper and Row Publishers, New York, 1970, pp. 303-308.

42. Y. Grunfeld and Z. Griliches, "Is Aggregation Necessarily Bad?", *The Review of Economics and Statistics*, February 1960, pp. 1-13.

43. Federal Power Commission, *Steam-Electric Plant Construction Cost*, p. XIII.

44. Federal Power Commission, *1970 National Power Survey*, p. IV-1-60.

45. *Ibid.*, p. IV-1-61.

46. See chapter 2, "Interpretation."

47. Data do exist for 1961 and 1962 also but were not included because

the generating plants were still experimental and the cost data consequently are unreliable.

48. Pumped hydroelectric plants first made a significant appearance in 1963 and in 1970 accounted for about 4.5 percent of all hydroelectric capacity in the United States.

49. Federal Power Commission, *1970 National Power Survey*, p. I-1-73 and p. I-1-78.

50. Federal Power Commission, *Hydroelectric Plant Construction Cost and Annual Production Expenses*, U.S. Government Printing Office, Washington, April 1973, p. VII.

51. Kendrick, *Postwar Productivity*, p. 349.

52. These programs are documented and a discussion of the technical aspects of the package can be found in H. I. Bowers, et. al., *CONCEPT–Computerized Conceptual Cost Estimates of Steam-Electric Power Plants*, Oak Ridge National Laboratory, ORNL-4809, April 1973.

53. United Engineers and Construction, Inc., *1000-MW(e) Central Station Power Plants Investment Study*, WASH-1230 (June 1972).

54. NUS Corporation, *Guide for Economic Evaluation of Nuclear Reactor Plant Designs*, NUS-531 (January 1969). This publication contains a description of the AEC's Middletown, USA site.

55. Building labor, heavy labor, bricklayers, carpenters, structural iron workers, plasterers, electrical workers, steam fitters, operations engineers, small tractor operators, large tractor operators, crane operators, air compressor operators, truck drivers, boiler makers, other crafts.

56. Channels, I-beams, W-flanges, re-bars, redimix concrete, plyform, and lumber.

57. Bowers, et al., *CONCEPT*.

58. Federal Power Commission, *Hydroelectric Plant Construction Cost*, p. VII.

59. Federal Power Commission, *1970 National Power Survey*, p. I-1-21.

60. Federal Power Commission, *Hydroelectric Power Resources of the United States, Developed and Undeveloped*, U.S. Government Printing Office, Washington, December 1972, p. xii.

61. *Ibid*., p. xiii.

62. Federal Power Commission, *1970 National Power Survey*, p. 1-19-4.

63. *Ibid*.

64. A discussion of the trade-offs involved in selecting thermal power plants or hydroelectric plants can be found in H. G. Van Der Tak, *The*

Economic Choice Between Hydroelectric and Thermal Power Developments, The John Hopkins University Press, Baltimore, 1966.

Chapter 5
Cost Projections for Electrical Energy

1. L. M. Olmsted, "24th Annual Electrical Industry Forecast," *Electrical World*, September 15, 1973, p. 51.

2. This value, computed from the Edison Electric Institute's *Statistical Yearbook* (various years) is about 0.51 for hydroelectric plants and about 0.52 for conventional fossil plants.

3. See the *Forecasts of Electrical Energy Demand to the Year 2000* from the Federal Power Commission dated August 24, 1973.

4. Olmsted, "24th Annual Electrical Industry Forecast," p. 50.

5. Federal Power Commission, *The 1970 National Power Survey*, U.S. Government Printing Office, Washington, December 1971, p. I-7-4.

6. Olmsted, "24th Annual Electrical Industry Forecast," pp. 51-52.

7. Federal Power Commission, *1970 National Power Survey*, p. I-4-40.

8. H. Theil, *Applied Economic Forecasting*, Rand-McNally & Company, Chicago, 1966, p. 7.

9. Federal Power Commission, *1970 National Power Survey*, p. I-4-40.

10. *Ibid.*, p. I-19-8.

11. *Ibid.*, p. I-19-3.

12. Beginning of the design and construction is defined as the date the order is placed for the nuclear steam supply system or the fossil-fueled steam generating equipment.

13. Robert W. Patterson, "The Strech Out in Power Plant Schedules," *Power Engineering*, vol. 75, no. 9 (September 1971), pp. 40-41.

14. *Ibid.*, p. 42.

15. National Petroleum Council, *U.S. Energy Outlook*, National Petroleum Council, Washington, December 1972, p. 255.

16. Patterson, "The Stretch Out," pp. 42-43.

17. Federal Power Commission, *1970 National Power Survey*, pp. I-1-73-I-1-75.

18. *Ibid.*, p. IV-1-35-IV-1-41.

19. *Ibid.*, p. IV-1-66.

20. Federal Power Commission, *Steam-Electric Plant Construction Cost and Annual Production Expenses–1971*, U.S. Government Printing Office, Washington, February 1973, pp. xv-xvi.

21. This was determined by looking at the cost estimates from CONCEPT for each type of fuel: coal, oil, and gas.

22. Federal Power Commission, *1970 National Power Survey*, p. I-18-29 and p. I-19-4.

23. The multiplicative constants are regionally as follows: 1.1 (NE), 1.1 (MA), 1.1 (ENC), 1.27 (WNC), 1.17 (SA), 1.17 (ESC), 1.27 (WSC), 1.2 (M), and 1.2 (P).

24. Federal Power Commission, *1970 National Power Survey*, p. I-18-3 and p. I-18-6.

25. *Ibid.*, p. I-7-21 and p. I-7-27.

26. *Ibid.*, p. I-19-6.

27. Federal Power Commission, *Electric Utility Depreciation Practices, Classes A and B Privately Owned Companies, 1966*, U.S. Government Printing Office, Washington, January 1970.

28. M. Nerlove, "Returns to Scale in Electricity Supply," in *Readings in Economic Statistics and Econometrics*, A. Zellner (ed.), Little, Brown and Company, Boston, 1968, p. 423.

29. W. D. Nordhaus, "The Allocation of Energy Resources," *Brookings Papers on Economic Activity* 3, 1973. Nordhaus uses capital defined in dollar terms, for example. See page 533 of his article.

30. Federal Power Commission, *Forecasts of Electric Energy*, Appendix 2, page 3 of 3.

31. From a paper by C. J. Cicchetti and W. J. Gillen, "Electricity Growth: Economic Incentives and Environmental Quality," in *Energy Conservation*, Committee on Interior and Insular Affairs, U.S. Senate, March 22 and 23, 1973, p. 193.

32. Federal Power Commission, *Forecasts of Electric Energy*, Appendix 2.

33. Federal Power Commission, *1970 National Power Survey*, p. I-18-21.

34. Federal Power Commission, *Hydroelectric Power Resources of the United States, Developed and Undeveloped*, U.S. Government Printing Office, Washington, December 1972, pp. xiv-xv.

35. Federal Power Commission, *Electric Utility Depreciation Practices*.

Chapter 6
An Intertemporal-Spatial Price Equilibrium Model

1. See chapter 18 of T. Takayama and G. G. Judge, *Spatial and Temporal Price and Allocation Models,* North-Holland Publishing Company, Amsterdam, 1971.

2. The use of the time variable can be confusing if one looks at it out of context. When the time variable was considered in, say, chapter 2 when demand curves were being estimated, it referred to annual observations. However, when the whole intertemporal-spatial equilibrium model is considered in the current chapter, the time variable refers to five year increments.

3. It might be more useful to think of this addition to capacity as occurring not instantaneously at periot *t* but as occurring rather in a continuous stream between some initial planning and construction period and period *t* when the requisite demand is realized. However, only those people consuming the electrical energy from this new capacity will be required to pay for it and not those who are consumers throughout the planning and construction period.

4. Joint Committee on Atomic Energy, *Understanding the "National Energy Dilemma"*, by the Staff of JCAE, 93rd Congress, 1st Session, 1973, p. 18.

5. One of the many discussions of these limitations for electrical energy in general can be found in the testimony of A. Radin, General Manager, American Public Power Association, in *Fuel and Energy Resources,* Committee on Interior and Insular Affairs, U.S. House of Representatives, 92nd Congress, 2nd Session, April 1972, p. 367.

6. F. P. Ramsey, "A Mathematical Theory of Savings," *The Economic Journal*, Vol. 38 (December 1928), pp. 553-555.

7. R. A. Schrimper, "Discussion: An Intertemporal Price Equilibrium Model," Journal of Farm Economics, vol. 46, no. 2 (May 1964), p. 485.

8. A. R. Prest and R. Turvey, "Cost Benefit Analysis: A Survey," American Economic Association and the Royal Economic Society, *Surveys of Economic Theory, Volume 3,* St. Martin's Press, New York, 1968, pp. 169-172.

9. W. J. Baumol, "On the Social Rate of Discount," *The American Economic Review,* vol. 58, no. 4 (September 1968), pp. 788-802.

10. Takayama and Judge, *Spatial and Temporal Price and Allocation Models,* p. 16.

11. *Ibid.*, p. 16 and also J. C. G. Boot, *Quadratic Programming,* Rand-McNally & Company, Chicago, 1964, pp. 36-39.

12. For a discussion of the Kuhn-Tucker conditions, see H. W. Kuhn and A. W. Tucker, "Nonlinear Programming," in *Proceedings of the Second Berkeley Symposium on Mathematical Statistics and Probability*, J. Neyman (ed.), University of California Press, Berkeley, 1951, pp. 481-492.

13. Boot, *Quadratic Programming*, pp. 28-30.

14. S. Marglin, "Objectives of Water Resource Development: A General Statement," in *Design of Water Resource Systems*, A. Maass (ed.), Harvard University Press, Cambridge, 1962, pp. 36-38.

15. Federal Power Commission, *Hydroelectric Power Resources of the United States, Developed and Undeveloped*, U.S. Government Printing Office, Washington, December 1972, p. vii.

16. W. N. Peach, *The Energy Outlook for the 1980's*, Joint Economic Committee, U.S. Government Printing Office, Washington, December 17, 1973, pp. 19-20.

17. R. Turvey, "Marginal Cost," *The Economic Journal*, vol. 79, no. 314, (June 1969), pp. 282-99.

18. F. P. Hall and G. N. Broderick, *Supply and Demand for Energy in the United States by States and Regions, 1960 and 1965 (2. Utility Electricity)* Information Circular 8402, U.S. Department of the Interior, Bureau of Mines, U.S. Government Printing Office, Washington, 1969, p. 9.

19. *Ibid.*, p. 10.

20. J. de V. Graaff, *Theoretical Welfare Economics*, Cambridge University Press, London, 1957, p. 122. This reference gives a concise discussion of the considerations.

21. This idea is fully discussed and proved in P. A. Samuelson, "The Gains from International Trade," *Canadian Journal of Economics and Political Science*, May 1939, pp. 195-205.

22. The whole consideration of the income distribution question is looked at by I. M. D. Little, *A Critique of Welfare Economics*, 2nd ed., Oxford University Press, Oxford, 1957, pp. 250-251.

23. This concept of spatial price discrimination is discussed more completely in B. H. Stevens and C. P. Rydell, "Spatial Demand Theory and Monopoly Price Policy," *Papers and Proceedings of the Regional Science Association*, vol. 17 (1966), pp. 201-202.

24. E. M. Hoover, "Spatial Price Discrimination," *The Review of Economic Studies*, vol. 4 (1937), pp. 182-191.

25. J. Henderson and R. E. Quandt, *Microeconomic Theory*, 2nd ed., McGraw-Hill Book Company, New York, 1971, pp. 264-267.

26. F. M. Scherer, *Industrial Market Structure and Economic Performance,* Rand-McNally & Company, Chicago, 1970, p. 15.

27. R. E. Caves and R. W. Jones, *World Trade and Payments,* Little, Brown and Company, Boston, 1973, pp. 206-210. This reference gives a diagrammatic exposition of the gains in welfare if one departs from a monopolistic market structure and lets perfect competition prevail.

Chapter 7
Conclusions

1. R. M. Nixon, *Presidential Energy Statements,* Committee on Interior and Insular Affairs, U.S. Senate, U.S. Government Printing Office, Washington, 1973, p. 9.

2. P. Sporn, *The Integrated Power System,* McGraw-Hill Book Company, New York, 1950.

3. This seems to be the implication in the discussion of the estimates. See pages I-18-21 through I-18-25 in *The 1970 National Power Survey,* by The Federal Power Commission, U.S. Government Printing Office, Washington, December 1971.

Bibliography

Allen, R.G.D., *Mathematical Economics,* St. Martin's Press, New York, 1960.

American Gas Association, *Gas Facts Yearbook,* New York, annual.

Anderson, D. "Models for Determining Least Cost Investments in Electricity Supply," *The Bell Journal of Economics and Management Science,* vol. 3, no. 1 (Spring 1972), pp. 267-299.

Anderson, K.P. *Toward Econometric Estimation of Industrial Energy Demand: An Experimental Application to the Primary Metals Industry,* R-719-NSF, Rand Corporation, Santa Monica, December 1971.

Balestra, P. and M. Nerlove, "Pooling Cross Section and Time Series Data in the Estimation of a Dynamic Model: The Demand for Natural Gas," *Econometrica,* vol. 34, no. 3 (July 1966), pp. 585-612.

Barzel, Y., "The Production Function and Technical Change in the Steam Power Industry," *The Journal of Political Economy,* 72 (April 1964), pp. 133-150.

Baughman, M.L., *Dynamic Energy System Modeling,* Unpublished Ph.D Thesis, M.I.T., 1972.

Baumol, W.J., "On the Social Rate of Discount," *The American Economic Review,* vol. 58, no. 4 (September 1968), pp. 788-802.

Baxter, R.E. and R. Rees, "An Analysis of the Industrial Demand for Electricity," *The Economic Journal,* vol. 78, no. 310 (June 1968), pp. 277-298.

Beer, F.A., "Energy, Environment, and International Integration," in *Growing Against Ourselves,* S.L. Kwee (ed.), Lexington Books, D.C. Heath and Company, Lexington, Mass., 1972.

Bhagwati, J., "The Pure Theory of International Trade: A Survey," American Economic Association and Royal Economic Society, *Surveys of Economic Theory, Volume 2,* St. Martin's Press, New York, 1965.

Boot, J.G.C., *Quadratic Programming,* Rand-McNally & Company, Chicago, 1964.

Bowers, H.I., et. al., *CONCEPT-Computerized Conceptual Cost Estimates of Steam-Electric Power Plants,* Oak Ridge National Laboratory, ORNL-4809, April 1973.

Bridge, J.L., *Applied Econometrics,* North-Holland Publishing Company, Amsterdam, 1971.

Caves, R.E. and R.W. Jones, *World Trade and Payments,* Little, Brown and Company, Boston, 1973.

Chapman, D., T. Tyrrell, and T. Mount, ''Electricity Demand Growth and the Energy Crisis,'' *Science,* vol. 178 (November 19, 1972), pp. 703-708.

Chetty, V.K., ''Pooling of Time Series and Cross Section Data,'' *Econometrica,* vol. 36, no. 2 (April 1968), pp. 279-289.

Christ, C., *Econometric Models and Methods,* John Wiley & Sons, New York, 1966.

Cicchetti, C.J. and W.J. Gillin, ''Electricity Growth: Economic Incentives and Environmental Quality,'' reprinted in *Energy Conservation,* Hearings before the Committee on Interior and Insular Affairs, U.S. Senate, March 22 and 23, 1973, pp. 181-206.

Cramer, J.S., *Empirical Econometrics,* North-Holland Publishing Company, Amsterdam, 1971.

Culberson, O., *The Consumption of Electricity in the United States,* Oak Ridge National Laboratory, ORNL-NSF-EP-5, June 1971.

Culbertson, L., *Professional Engineer,* New York, February 1971.

Currie, J.M., J.A. Murphy, and A. Schmitz, ''The Concept of Economic Surplus and Its Use in Economic Analysis,'' *The Economic Journal,* vol. 81, no. 324 (December 1971), pp. 741-799.

Dhrymes, P., *Econometrics,* Harper and Row Publishers, New York, 1970.

———, *Distributed Lags: Problems of Estimation and Formulation,* Holden-Day, San Francisco, 1971.

———, and M. Kurz, ''Technology and Scale in Electricity Generation,'' *Econometrica,* vol. 32, no. 3 (July 1964), pp. 287-315.

Doctor, R.D., et. al., *California's Electricity Quandry: III Slowing the Growth Rate,* R-1116-NSF/CSA, Rand Corporation, Santa Monica, September 1972.

Duchesneau, T., *Interfuel Substitutibility in the Electric Utility Sector of the U.S. Economy,* U.S. Government Printing Office, Washington, 1972.

Edison Electric Institute, *Statistical Yearbook of the Electric Utility Industry,* New York, annual.

Enke, S., ''Equilibrium Among Spatially Separated Markets: Solution by Electric Analogue,'' *Econometrica,* vol. 19, no. 1 (January 1951), pp. 40-47.

Evans, M. K., *Macroeconomic Activity: Theory, Forecasting, and Control,* Harper and Row Publishers, New York, 1969.

Federal Power Commission, *Electric Utility Depreciation Practices, Classes A and B Privately Owned Companies, 1966,* U.S. Government Printing Office, Washington, January 1970.

———, *The 1970 National Power Survey,* U.S. Government Printing Office, Washington, December, 1971.

———, *Statistics of Privately Owned Electric Utilities in the United States, Classes A and B Companies,* U.S. Government Printing Office, Washington, October 1972.

———, *Hydroelectric Power Resources of the United States, Developed and Undeveloped,* U.S. Government Printing Office, Washington, December 1972.

———, *Steam-Electric Plant Construction Cost and Annual Production Expenses, Twenty-Fourth Annual Supplement, 1971,* U.S. Government Printing Office, Washington, February 1973.

———, *Hydroelectric Plant Construction Cost and Annual Production Expenses,* U.S. Government Printing Office, Washington, April 1973.

———, *Forecasts of Electric Energy and Demand to the Year 2000, A Report by the Task Force on Forecast Review to the Technical Advisory Committee on Power Supply, National Power Survey,* Unpublished, August 24, 1973.

Feldstein, M.S., "Equity and Efficiency in Public Sector Pricing: The Optimal Two Part Tariff," *The Quarterly Journal of Economics,* vol. 86, no. 2 (May 1972), pp. 175-187.

Fisher, F. and C. Kaysen, *A Study in Econometrics: The Demand for Electricity in the United States,* North-Holland Publishing Company, Amsterdam, 1962.

Galatin, M., *Economies of Scale and Technological Change in Thermal Power Generation,* North-Holland Publishing Company, 1968.

Goldberger, A. *Econometric Theory,* John Wiley & Sons, New York, 1964.

Graaff, J. de V., *Theoretical Welfare Economics,* Cambridge University Press, London, 1957.

Graham, R.E., et. al., "State Projection of Income, Employment and Population," *Survey of Current Business,* vol. 52, no. 4 (April 1972), pp. 22-48.

Griliches, Z., "Distributed Lags: A Survey," *Econometrica,* vol. 35, no. 1 (January 1967), pp. 16-49.

Grunfeld, Y. and Z. Griliches, "Is Aggregation Necessarily Bad?" *The Review of Economics and Statistics,* vol. 42 (February 1960), pp. 1-13.

Haavelmo, T. "The Statistical Implications of a System of a Simultaneous Equations," *Econometrica,* vol. 11, no. 1 (January 1943), pp. 1-12.

Hall, F. P. and G. N. Broderick, *Supply and Demand for Energy in the United States by States and Regions, 1960 and 1965 (2. Utility*

Electricity), Information Circular 8402, U.S. Department of the Interior, Bureau of Mines, U.S. Government Printing Office, Washington, 1969.

Henderson, J. and R. E. Quandt, *Microeconomic Theory,* 2nd ed., McGraw-Hill Book Company, New York, 1971.

Hoover, E. M., "Spatial Price Discrimination," *The Review of Economic Studies,* vol. 4 (1937), pp. 182-191.

Hopkins, D. S. P., "Sufficient Conditions for Optimality in Infinite Horizon Linear Economic Models," Technical Report No. 69-3, Stanford University, 1969.

Houthakker, H. S., "Additive Preferences," *Econometrica,* vol. 28, no. 2 (April 1960), pp. 244-257.

———, "New Evidence on Demand Elasticities," *Econometrica,* vol. 33, no. 2 (April 1965), pp. 277-288.

———, and P. Verlager, "The Demand for Gasoline: A Mixed Cross Sectional and Time Series Analysis, Unpublished, May 1973.

———, and D. P. Sheehan, "Dynamic Demand Analysis for Gasoline and Residential Electricity," Paper presented at the American Economic Association Meetings, New York, December 1973.

Johnston, J., *Statistical Cost Analysis,* McGraw-Hill Book Company, New York, 1960.

Judge, G. G. and T. Takayama, *Studies in Economic Planning Over Space and Time,* North-Holland Publishing Company, Amsterdam, 1973.

Kahn, A., *The Economics of Regulation, Volume 1,* John Wiley & Sons, New York, 1970.

Kendrick, J., *Postwar Productivity Trends in the United States, 1948-1969,* National Bureau of Economic Research, New York, 1973.

Kmenta, J., *Elements of Econometrics,* Macmillan Company, New York, 1971.

Komiya, R., "Technological Progress and the Production Function in the United States Steam Power Industry," *The Review of Economics and Statistics,* vol. 44 (May 1962), pp. 156-166.

Koopmans, T., *Activity Analysis of Production and Allocation,* John Wiley & Sons, New York, 1951.

———, *Three Essays on the State of Economic Science,* McGraw-Hill Book Company, New York, 1957.

Kuh, E., "The Validity of Cross Sectionally Estimated Behavior Equations in Time Series Applications," *Econometrica,* vol. 27, no. 2 (April 1949), pp. 172-214.

Kuhn, H. W. and A. W. Tucker, "Nonlinear Programming," in *Proceedings of the Second Berkeley Symposium on Mathematical*

Statistics and Probability, J. Neyman (ed.), University of California Press, Berkeley, 1951, pp. 481-492.

Lee, T. C. and S. K. Seaver, "A Positive Model of Spatial Equilibrium with Special Reference to the Broiler Markets," in *Studies in Economic Planning Over Space and Time,* G. G. Judge and T. Takayama (eds.), North-Holland Publishing Company, Amsterdam, 1973, pp. 443-463.

Little, I. M. D., *A Critique of Welfare Economics,* 2nd ed., Oxford University Press, Oxford, 1957.

Littlechild, S. C., "Marginal Cost Pricing with Joint Costs," *The Economic Journal,* vol. 80, no. 318 (June 1970), pp. 323-335.

Liviatan, N., "Consistent Estimation of Distributed Lags," *International Economic Review,* vol. 4, no. 1 (January 1963), pp. 44-52.

Madansky, A., "The Fitting of Straight Lines When Both Variables Are Subject to Error," *The Journal of the American Statistical Association,* vol. 54 (March 1959), pp. 173-205.

Marglin, S., "Objectives of Water Resource Development: A General Statement," in *Design of Water Resource Systems,* A. Maass (ed.), Harvard University Press, Cambridge, 1962, pp. 17-87.

Meadows, D. H., et. al., *The Limits to Growth: A Report for the Club of Rome's Project on the Predicament of Mankind,* New American Library, New York, 1972.

Mount, T. D., L. D. Chapman, and T. J. Tyrrell, *Electricity Demand in the United States: An Econometric Analysis,* Oak Ridge National Laboratory, ORNL-NSF-EP-49, June 1973.

National Petroleum Council, *U.S. Energy Outlook,* National Petroleum Council, Washington, December 1972.

Nerlove, M., *Estimation and Identification of Cobb-Douglas Production Functions,* Rand-McNally & Company, Chicago, 1965.

———, "Returns to Scale In Electricity Supply," in *Readings in Economic Statistics and Econometrics,* A. Zellner (ed.), Little, Brown and Company, Boston, 1968.

Nordhaus, W.D., "The Allocation of Energy Resources," *Brookings Papers on Economic Activity 3,* 1973, pp. 529-570.

Nourse, H. O., *Regional Economics,* McGraw-Hill Book Company, New York, 1968.

NUS Corporation, *Guide for Economic Evaluation of Nuclear Reactor Plant Designs,* NUS-531, January 1969.

Olmsted, L. M., "24th Annual Electrical Industry Forecast," *Electrical World,* September 15, 1973, pp. 39-54.

Patterson, R. W., "The Stretch Out in Power Plant Schedules," *Power Engineering,* vol. 75, no. 9 (September 1971), pp. 40-43.

Peach, W. N., *The Energy Outlook for the 1980's,* Joint Economic Committee, U.S. Government Printing Office, Washington, December 17, 1973.

Perloff, H. S., et. al., *Regions, Resources, and Economic Growth,* University of Nebraska Press, Lincoln, 1960.

Plessner, Y., "Activity Analysis, Quadratic Programming, and General Equilibrium," *International Economic Review,* vol. 8, no. 2 (June 1967), pp. 168-179.

Pressman, I., "A Mathematical Formulation of the Peak-Load Pricing Problem," *The Bell Journal of Economics and Management Science,* vol. 1, no. 2 (Autumn 1970), pp. 304-326.

Prest, A. R. and R. Turvey, "Cost-Benefit Analysis: A Survey," American Economic Association and Royal Economic Society, *Surveys of Economic Theory, Volume 3,* St. Martin's Press, New York, 1968.

Ramsey, F. P., "A Mathematical Theory of Savings," *The Economic Journal,* vol. 38 (December 1928), pp. 543-559.

Samuelson, P. A., "The Gains from International Trade," *Canadian Journal of Economics and Political Science,* May 1939, pp. 195-205.

———, "Spatial Price Equilibrium and Linear Programming," *The American Economic Review,* vol. 42 (June 1952), pp. 283-303.

———, "Intertemporal Price Equilibrium: A Prologue to the Theory of Speculation," *Weltwirtschaftliches Archiv,* vol. 79 (1957), pp. 181-221.

Scherer, F. M., *Industrial Market Structure and Economic Performance,* Rand-McNally & Company, Chicago, 1970.

Schmookler, J., "Economic Sources of Inventive Activity," *The Journal of Economic History,* March 1962, pp. 1-20.

Schrimper, R. A., "Discussion: An Intertemporal Price Equilibrium Model," *Journal of Farm Economics,* vol. 46, no. 2 (May 1964), pp. 484-486.

Shows, E. W. and R. H. Burton, *Microeconomics,* Lexington Books, D. C. Heath and Company, Lexington, Mass. 1972.

Solow, R. M., "Technological Change and the Aggregate Production Function," *The Review of Economics and Statistics,* August 1957, pp. 312-320.

Sporn, P., *The Integrated Power System,* McGraw-Hill Book Company, New York, 1950.

Stevens, B. H. and C. P. Rydell, "Spatial Demand Theory and Monopoly Price Policy," *Papers and Proceedings of the Regional Science Association,* vol. 17 (1966), pp. 195-204.

Suits, D. B., "Use of Dummy Variables in Regression Equations," *The Journal of the American Statistical Association,* vol. 52 (December 1957), pp. 548-551.

Takayama, T. and G. G. Judge, "An Intertemporal Price Equilibrium Model," *Journal of Farm Economics,* vol. 46, no. 2 (May 1964), pp. 477-486.

———, "Equilibrium Among Spatially Separated Markets: A Reformulation," *Econometrica,* vol. 32. no. 4 (October 1964), pp. 510-524.

———, *Spatial and Temporal Price and Allocation Models,* North-Holland Publishing Company, Amsterdam, 1971.

Takayama, T., and A. D. Woodland, "Equivalence of Price and Quantity Formulations of Spatial Equilibrium: Purified Duality in Quadratic and Concave Programming," *Econometrica,* vol. 38, no. 6 (November 1970), pp. 889-906.

Texas Eastern Transmission Corporation, *Competition and Growth in the U.S. Energy Markets, 1947-1985,* Texas Eastern Transmission Corporation, Houston, 1968.

Theil, H. "Specification Errors and the Estimation of Economic Relationships," *Review of the International Statistical Institute,* vol. 25, no. 1/3 (1957), pp. 41-51.

———, *Economic Forecasts and Policy,* 2nd ed., North-Holland Publishing Company, Amsterdam, 1965.

———, *Applied Economic Forecasting,* Rand-McNally & Company, Chicago, 1966.

———, *Principles of Econometrics,* John Wiley & Sons, New York, 1971.

Turvey, R., *Optimal Pricing and Investment in Electricity Supply,* George Allen and Unwin, London, 1968.

———, "Marginal Cost," *The Economic Journal,* vol. 79, no. 314 (June 1969), pp. 282-299.

Tyrrell, T. J. and D. Chapman, "Demand for Electricity: The Ohio Test Region and the United States (1970-2000)," Unpublished, August 1972.

United Engineers and Construction, Inc., *1000-MW(e) Central Station Power Plants Investment Study,* WASH-1230, June 1972.

U.S. Congress, House, Committee on Interior and Insular Affairs, *Fuel and Energy Resources,* 92nd Congress, 2nd Session, April 1972.

———, *Energy "Demand" Studies: An Analysis and Appraisal,* 92nd Congress, 2nd Session, September 1972.

U.S. Congress, House, Committee on Interstate and Foreign Commerce, *Power Plant Siting and Environmental Protection, Part I,* 92nd Congress, 1st Session, May 1971.

U.S. Congress, Joint Committee on Atomic Energy, *Understanding the "National Energy Dilemma",* by the staff of JCAE, 93rd Congress, 1st Session, 1973.

U.S. Congress, Senate, Committee on Interior and Insular Affairs,

Summary Report of the Cornell Workshop on Energy and the Environment, 92nd Congress, 2nd Session, May 1972.

———, *Survey of Energy Consumption Projections,* 92nd Congress, 2nd Session, 1972.

U.S. Department of Commerce, Bureau of Economic Analysis, *Statistical Abstract of the United States,* U.S. Government Printing Office, Washington, 1971.

U.S. President, *Messages from the President of the United States Concerning Energy Resources,* U.S. Government Printing Office, Washington, April 18, 1973.

U.S. Senate, Committee on Interior and Insular Affairs, *Presidential Energy Statements,* U.S. Government Printing Office, Washington, 1973.

Van Der Tak, H. G. *The Economic Choice Between Hydroelectric and Thermal Power Developments,* The Johns Hopkins University Press, Baltimore, 1966.

Waverman, L., *Natural Gas and National Policy,* University of Toronto Press, Toronto, 1973.

Wilcox, C., *Public Policies Toward Business,* Richard D. Irwin, Homewood, Ill., 1971.

Wilson, J. W., "Residential Demand for Electricity," *The Quarterly Review of Economics and Statistics,* vol. 11, no. 1 (Spring 1971), pp. 7-22.

Working, E. J., "What Do Statistical 'Demand Curves' Show?," *The Quarterly Journal of Economics,* vol. 41 (May 1927), pp. 212-235.

Zellner, A., "An Efficient Method of Estimating Seemingly Unrelated Regressions and Tests for Aggregation Bias," *The Journal of the American Statistician Association,* vol. 57 (June 1962), pp. 348-368.

Index

About the Author

Noel D. Uri received the A.B. from San Diego State University in mathematics in 1967 and the M.A. in economics in 1969. In 1974 he received the Ph.D. in economics from the University of Illinois at Urbana-Champaign. Dr. Uri is employed by the U.S. Department of Labor, Bureau of Labor Statistics, Office of Research Methods and Standards.